BR
THE MAGIC
IN YOUR MIND

Explains the latent powers of your mind,
and shows how they can be harnessed
to bring you prosperity, success,
health and vitality.

BRING OUT THE MAGIC IN YOUR MIND

by

AL KORAN

THORSONS PUBLISHERS LIMITED
Wellingborough, Northamptonshire

First published 1964
Sixth Impression 1969
First Paperback Edition 1972
Ninth Impression 1984

ISBN 0 7225 1181 7

Printed and Bound in Great Britain by
Whitstable Litho Ltd., Whitstable, Kent

Contents

Introduction 9

1 The Magic Of Belief 13

2 How Belief Works 19

3 The Magic Of Visualization 32

4 Power Of The Subconscious 46

5 Silence And Meditation 56

6 The Magic Of Love 65

7 The Secret Of Wealth 81

8 The Magic Of Friendship 97

9 The Magic Of Change 108

10 The Magic Of Charms And Mascots 115

11 The Magic Of Right Impressions 122

12 The Magic Of Laughter 133

13 The Magic Of Colour 143

14 The Magic Of Flowers 154

15 The Magic Of Right Habits 163

16 The Magic Of Music 170

17 Have Done With Fear 177

18 The Magic Of Happiness 188

19 The Magic Of Romance 199

20 Health That Brings Magic 211

21 The Magic Of Time 226

22 Help Through Your Hobby 241

23 Observing The Wonderful 249

24 Prelude To Mind-Reading—Physiognomy 260

25 Prelude To Mind-Reading—Numerology 266

26 Prelude To Mind-Reading—Astrology 274

27 I Call It PURE PSYCHOLOGY 282

Introduction

AT the early age of seven, it was apparent that I had the extra-sensory instincts and uncanny sixth-sense which has today earned me the title of **The World's Greatest Mind-Reader** and **The Finest Mental Magician in the World.**

Even at this tender age I was able to state the whereabouts of my Aunt's lost engagement ring, simply because I had 'seen' it in the drawer of her dressing-table.

School days had their problems for me, for by this time I had acquired such an instinct that, in mathematics, I knew the answers to sums without working them out. My headmaster put me through many tests; as he got all the right answers this made my parents and my teacher realize that here was no ordinary schoolboy, and my unusual ability was encouraged.

I read all I could about magic, fantasy and mystery, and at fifteen became the youngest member of the Magicians' Club. Having made history in this way, I made it again the following year by being the youngest member ever to win their gold medal.

After appearing in many concerts and studying astrology, psychology, and Yoga (under a Tibetan Monk then living in England) I decided that my future career lay, not in conjuring but in that more intangible field of the magic of the mind.

On many occasions I have, through extra-sensory perception, given predictions that have astounded the public. At a dinner given by the press, I wrote the next day's headlines of a certain newspaper, **and I was right.** In cabaret I wrote the results of a General Election on a blackboard before they were known, **and I was right.** On BBC TV I wrote the first, second, and third horses in the 2,000 Guineas (a race which was not to be held for another two weeks), **and I was right again.**

I have read minds and told people where they are going for their holidays, how many people are in the family, their names, birthdays, and many other things. **And I am always right.** I have baffled millions of people on stage, and television viewers in their homes, in this country and abroad. And millions are left wondering. How do I read minds? How do I do this, and how do I do that? Magic? Trickery? Mind-Reading? Conjuring? Accomplices in the audience? Sleight of hand? What is the secret?

I tell them it is **pure psychology.** I scorn the use of stooges and any form of organized assistance.

This brings me to what I am getting at. From all over the world, people bombard me with letters, telegrams, and phone calls. They come backstage at the theatre. I have now had to keep my home address a secret. Not even my friends know where I live. It is essential that my private life be free of challengers who only wish me to tell them how to win the pools and to tell them the winner of the 4.30.

I have great respect for my power and will do nothing which could be used for evil. I never bet on any race whose winner I know, nor will I hand out tips to others.

People plead with me to help them win a fortune; win the gamble which is going to open up a joyous, care-free life for them at last.

Why do people want to win the pools? Do they want to get away from it all, to spend lazy days on the sun-kissed beaches of tropical islands? Or tingle to the crystal clearness of the air and breathtaking vistas of snow-fringed lakes and mountains?

Perhaps they want a large and luxurious house, and servants to wait on them. They are tired. If a woman, she is tired of the cooking, the washing, the ironing, the making of beds, the shopping, the waiting in queues. If a man, he is tired of his routine business, and all the strain and worry of it. He has been doing too much.

Tired, frustrated, tensed, and depressed. Sick people all wanting a way out, an escape from it all.

And that is why I am writing this book. Its purpose is to help you resolve your problems by proving to you that there is magic in **your** mind, only waiting to be drawn out. I want to tell you how to attain all your wildest dreams.

For most people and nations, things are always happening which they do not want to happen. **I will bring the magic out of your mind,** so that only the things you **want** to happen will come true.

By the power of this magic in your mind, once it is released, you will have that gleaming car, that luxurious house, that holiday in the sun. Why spend time and money on the pools, why gamble on horses or bingo? You can have that fabulous wealth without spending your time and money like that. And it will be much more satisfying. Every day will be an exciting, happy day, when you will work magic for yourself.

Forget the pools, forget the horses, forget the bingo. You have a power just as magical as Aladdin's Lamp or Alf's Button. It is a dynamic power with the riches of a goldmine, when you know how to use it. This book is to set you on the road.

1
The Magic Of Belief

'MUMMIE, what makes people clever? Why are some cleverer than others? . . . Mummie, why do some boys die before they've grown right up? . . . Mummie, why do they make poison if it kills people? . . . Why are some people nice and others horrid? Once upon a time there were three bears? Why, Mummie, why? . . .'

As a child, my mind was besieged with perplexities; I was always questioning, questioning, struggling in my enquiring disposition to unravel mysteries that had baffled others far, far beyond my years all through the ages.

In a different degree, I suppose that my curiosity has stayed with me through the passing years; for although many perplexities have been resolved for me, others have come to take their place. It is the way with psychologists, the way of anyone who would probe the magic powers of the mind. The seed of curiosity, once it is born, is with you all your life and wherever you are. You can be in the Himalayas, or you can be in the Underground at Piccadilly. The workings of the mind – **your** mind, and the minds of other people – are of such complexity, but so infinitely fascinating to study that, once you have started to probe their mysteries, you never cease to marvel, and the claims of one upon your wonderment are as great as those of another. In their different ways, the lady who professes that a copper bangle around her wrist has cured her of the scourge of rheumatism is of no less interest and wonderment to you than the Fire Walkers of the Fiji Islands, who will walk with bare feet on red-hot cinders. And the ceremonial dances of the Indians when they invoke the rains constitute a spectacle no more awe-inspiring than that of thousands of people travelling to Lourdes.

Such demonstrations, to me, at least, who has witnessed them, have been equal in both the sense of wonderment and curiosity that they have exercised upon me. You may gaze, as I have done, upon old men and women, many of them crippled, toiling up a mountain merely for the privilege of worshipping at a Holy Shrine, and you may ask yourself, 'What makes them do it?' just as you may marvel that people being baptized in icy water can come up, giving cry to 'Alleluia!' even though their teeth be chattering and their bodies shaking.

I wonder sometimes, when I reflect upon the endless string of questions that I placed before the wisdom of my mother, if she ever guessed that during the years which were to follow in my development to manhood, my insatiable curiosity for delving into the magic of the mind would lead me to attend meetings of a scientific, spiritual and occult nature, and that with that same insatiable curiosity I should try to get into the minds of great men and women of history by reading and making myself familiar with their lives. Would she guess, too, that I should meet and speak with many outstanding person-alities in all lines of human endeavour, searching, searching for the answer of what it was that had taken them to the top?

Well, I am going to tell you right away, that my one great discovery in all this searching and curiosity has been that in them all there was a 'something' that worked magic, and that 'something' is Belief. The magic of Belief grants phenomenal results for all who accept it; belief takes you where you want to go with the speed of jet propulsion. As a millionaire once

14

said to me, 'Before I leap out of bed, I always say, **"I believe, I believe, I believe"**. Three times, just like that. And I am never in a tailspin.'

From official records which are kept, it is known that at least six thousand cures have happened at Lourdes. Every case of miraculous healing is investigated so as to eradicate every chance of charlatanism. People gaze in wonder and rapture before the Basilica – and **believe**.

Let me tell you about Gabriel Gargam, paralysed from the waist downwards, his spine severely injured. Doctors knew that there was no aid that medical science could offer. Gargam struggled to move, but could not do so. The doctors shook their heads.

His mother said, 'My son, I want you to go to Lourdes.'

Gabriel did not want to go all that way.

But mother insisted. So he arrived at Lourdes, though his nurse feared the worst.

Then suddenly, to everyone's amazement, Gabriel Gargam raised himself to his feet. Within twenty-four hours he was walking well. Medical examination by sixty doctors showed that this complete cure could not be explained scientifically. Back at home he resumed his job normally.

What had brought about the miraculous change?

He suddenly **believed**.

There are many cases as wonderful as this one.

To bring out the magic in your mind, Belief is the very first essential.

There was a young man in financial difficulties who approached his wealthy brother for the loan of only a pound or two. The brother, in a temper, said, 'Go jump off the pier.'

The brother did not believe, so would not help. He looked upon it as mere cadging. The Greatest Psychologist the world has ever known **believed** in human nature, even when it was nailing Him to one of His own trees.

You have not only got to believe in yourself, but you have

15

got to believe in the other fellow. You cannot bring the magic out of your mind in any other way.

It is the **belief** within you that brings outwards the material results.

Take the case of a busy housewife who woke up one morning feeling like nothing on earth. The thought of the large family wash awaiting her filled her with dread. But suddenly she remembered an energy tablet that a friend had given to her, with the assurance that it was a wonder cure for tiredness. It's still in my apron pocket, she thought, so she dug down and found it, then popped it into her mouth. In a few minutes she started work; the big wash was child's play. She finished it, then polished all the floors, and cleaned the windows. Life was wonderful. All that from one tablet!

Then she put her hand in her pocket and found the tablet; she had swallowed a sweet her child had given her.

You see, her **belief** brought the magic which changed her day, and even took away her tiredness. She had brought out the magic in her mind, simply by **believing**.

A few years ago, while I was in hospital, a man in the bed next to mine had his right hand absolutely covered with warts. The doctors were cutting and cauterizing them. Then a patient came up one day and asked the fellow, 'Would you like me to get rid of the warts on your hand?' He said, 'Oh, please.'

'I will count them for you, and then they will disappear.'

He did, and we thought no more about it. But in a week the whole mass of warts had disappeared. Through the magic of **Belief**.

I told this story to a group of doctors one day, and a lady friend of mine shrugged her shoulders, grunted and said, 'Preposterous.'

She had no belief.

Dr D. G. Aitken of Cumberland, recently reported in the British medical magazine the *Practitioner*, that he cured children's warts by buying them for a few pennies each, and telling the children the blemishes would disappear. Aitken wrote that the result had been 'quite astounding'. It was **Belief**, of course.

Many well-educated men and women in their respective fields will, in their ignorance, condemn the idea of *thought power*. It comes from the Far East, and we are born of the West. So they throw away their chances of success as people did in the long ago when Tibetans brought us the ancient secrets of magic. What a fool cannot learn, he laughs at. He will not believe because the light comes from too far a distance.

Yet the magis of the East have the most beautiful homes imaginable, and are surrounded by all the luxuries of the world. They know how to work the law of Creation. They are said to possess the ancient secrets of the lost civilization of Atlantis. It is true that nothing but the possession of these secrets could account for the fabulous wealth at their command.

These secrets, these laws, have not been lost. They are brought regularly from the East to the West for those who are ready to accept them.

If things are not happy and prosperous with you, it is not too late. **Belief** is the magic formula.

Tell anyone how you hope to get this and get that by magic, and they will throw cold water over you, as it were. They will laugh and think you crazy. They will drop doubts in your way and close your channels with their negative words.

It was exactly the same two thousand years ago. The Greatest Psychologist knew this. He knew that such knowledge was only for those who were ready to accept it. That is why, when the Disciples were taught how to work miracles (magic) through the wonderful power of **Belief**, they were given the secret and sent forth with the words:

'Go, **but tell no man.**'

It is when you tell other people that troubles begin. They tease, they laugh, they ridicule, they put every stumbling-block in the way to prevent you carrying out your plans.

In using this science (which is given you with the complete knowledge that no matter how you use it, you will get results), I give you a warning. Never use it for harmful or evil purposes. Since the beginning of man there have been two great forces at work; good and evil. Both are terrifically powerful in their respective cycles. I cannot emphasize this too strongly. If you employ your magic for harmful or evil purposes, **it will boomerang and destroy you.** These are not idle words. They are very solemn words. Black magic and white magic are based on the same principles.

Bring out the magic in your mind, by a strong **Belief.** I have belief, or I would fail every time.

I gave a performance under Fleet Street's sharpest eyes, the same as I have done on the stage.

Without benefit of lights, audience, or all the makings of illusion that are present when people are seeking entertainment in the evening, I gave a performance to these hard-boiled, sceptical journalists and this is what I did.

From the fingers of three prominent newspaper men I took three gold signet rings, threaded them on a pencil, and – before you could say **Koran** – the rings were suspended from the pencil linked in a chain yet unbroken.

Each of the owners identified his ring before they were returned intact.

How did I do it? I would not tell. But what I will say is that I would never attempt anything so seemingly incredible, if I had no belief. All magicians have belief, otherwise they would make fools of themselves. Belief is the most important thing to anyone who wants to work magic.

2
How Belief Works

THERE are certain people who have a baneful habit of constantly analysing everything. You can say that a thing works, but it is not enough. Before they can really accept a thing, they must analyse it, dissect it, pull it to pieces, tear it apart. They have no belief unless they can be made to **see how it works.** They are the people who crawl under cars, pull the clock to pieces, and bring out the microscope on every possible occasion. **How does it work?** Tell them that and they will believe.

First of all then, let us turn the analysis on self. What are **you**? You are just so much electricity. Go in the dark and comb your hair vigorously. If you are in good health you will hear the crackles and see the sparks fly out. That is the **electricity** in you.

The world is full of electricity – magnetic substance. Take an amber bead and keep rubbing it hard. By the electricity you have generated, your little amber bead is at once magnetic to minute pieces of paper. Similarly, a sheet of brown paper which has been held before the fire and is brushed hard will adhere to the wall or any flat surface. Why? Because it has become magnetized by the electricity you have generated.

What is that to do with bringing out the magic in your mind? Well, **everything**.

Electricity attracts, makes you **magnetic**, draws things to you. You don't stir up the electricity within you, stand in front of a brand new car and draw it to you, just like that. There is much more to it than that. I am only trying to make you conscious that electricity counts. It is a vital part of what brings the magic out of your mind, so that you can get the things that you want. Some people who are ill in bed are told that it is a consoling thing to have a cat for company, and stroke it. So the pet is put on the bed and they stroke it and stroke it and stroke it. But the reason really is that, by stroking the cat, they get some of the electricity from its body, and this helps to strengthen them and get them better.

The power to attract is within you, but you must be ever conscious that you possess it. There must be a constant **awareness**. You must know how to generate it to create, not repel, and that is what I am going to tell you about.

The Pole from North to South, running through the centre of the earth, is **magnetized**, whether you knew it before or not. And in like manner the human body is a magnet.

There are many ways in which you can generate this magnetism. One is to see that you sleep with the head of the bed North, so that you are **parallel** with the magnetic Pole running through the earth, and not lying **across** it. This is very important, for in this way the magnetic currents move from the head to the feet, and you get **full capacity**, instead of merely a slice across the body. Some people wonder why they are so restless and often cannot sleep. **This could be the answer,** they are lying in opposition.

So important is this North to South parallel that some people who really do accomplish the most magical things (because they have the know-how) make it a ritual to **face North** when they send out any dynamic thought-wish. No kidding, believe me, there are people who make a point of being in alignment with the earth's magnetic current so that their own magnetic powers are amplified.

Crazy, I can't swallow that, you say. But what is foolishness in the eyes of men is wisdom to the Tibetans.

You smile. You still have your doubts. This is all new and fanciful to you.

Scepticism is imperfect knowledge. It is in a sense slow suicide.

The poet Novalie says, 'To become imperfectly acquainted with a truth, we must first have disbelieved it.' So there is hope for you.

Difficult to grasp? Difficult to believe? **It was difficult two thousand years ago.**

The White Queen in **Alice through the Looking Glass** practised believing the impossible. She believed as many as six impossible things before breakfast!

Be positive. Believe.

A masseuse told me how he could see magnetic currents in the Universe. Some days he said these currents seem to move faster than others. They appear white and look like fine rain coming down, he said. Then he told me that some of his patients could see these currents.

He always made it a practice to keep the head of his massage table to the magnetic North, so as to use the currents to the best advantage. One of my patients was so sensitive to the North-South position, he said, that if the table was only a few inches off magnetic North, she sensed it; and upon checking it with his compass, he found she was right every time.

You must be **constantly aware** that, just as the earth is magnetized, so the human body is a magnet charged with electricity. Didn't you know that there is a mighty power in the world the scientists call electro-magnetism? Didn't you know that everything is electro-magnetic? The laws of attracting and repelling operate electro-magnetically.

This is an important thing to remember, if you want to

21

bring out the magic in your mind. Don't kid yourself, belief cannot work magic unless you are conscious of the fact that you have a drawing power, and do everything you can to make it stronger and stronger.

Are you perfectly happy with your position in life? Are you enjoying life to its fullest extent? Are you getting all the things in life you want?

So much depends on how you relax. Do you sit with your legs crossed, your arms folded, or your hands clasped? If you do it is fatal. **This cuts off your receiving power**, and makes you negative. Remember never to cross your legs, if possible, fold your arms or clasp your hands. Be awake all the time to what you want, and what you must do to receive the power to get it. There are times, of course, when you want to cut off bad influences; suppose someone is arguing or trying to pick a quarrel. Discordant thoughts are not for you, and you must cut off the power of evil by crossing your legs, folding your arms, and clasping your hands.

If you have an analytical mind you will like to probe into this truth of electricity.

Look to the Bible. It is full of it. When the Great Master of Magic walked on the water, the light all around was dazzling. He who did the seemingly impossible always appeared surrounded with great brilliance; surrounded by **electro-magnetism.**

The Angel of the Resurrection whose face was like lightning struck terror into the hearts of the sentry guard, in which there were perhaps four or six men. There was something terrific in this light to frighten those hardened Roman soldiers. It was **electricity.** A star might change, but a ray of light could never change. It goes on and on, even as your thoughts are going, through space, never altering its speed, never destroyed. Light goes on for ever. That's how dynamic electricity is, the light you generate within yourself.

The North of the magnetic pole is positive, and the South is negative. Every time you are negative in your thoughts and words, you automatically **separate yourself** from your electro-magnetism. A positive condition is always a magnetic condition; a condition that brings out the magic.

Belief is a positive word, and therefore creative. Everything positive is alive and works. Everything negative is dead, and has no creative power whatever. Negative means reject; to put aside, not to be used.

You must **polarize** your thoughts and words. It means learning to think differently, and speak differently. There must be a complete switch-over from negative attitudes to positive ones, from **I don't know what to believe** to **I believe.**

I can't make head or tail of it, you say.

Try it.

Like Edison said when they asked him about what electricity was. He said he could not explain, but . . . **try it.**

Now back to the Fiji Islands and the Fire Walkers. How do they do it? Magic, of course.

Well, for one thing, there is a ten days' course of **purification,** and one of the things they put great importance on is breathing. They will go out into the open, put up their hands, and take in deep breaths of air. Then they will appear to grasp at an invisible 'something' as though they were trying desperately to catch this electro-magnetism. They attach great importance to deep breathing and trying to catch the air. They do this to lift themselves into a higher dimension, and I think they do.

There is much more to it than that, but I want to emphasize the importance of deep breathing to anyone who wants to work magic.

What else do they do? They practise self-discipline. It is a part of their preparation. When the ten days' course is over they are able to heal the sick, make barren women give birth, and many magical things. The Fire Walkers are in complete ecstasy as they walk over the burning cinders. If flames leap up in front of them they continue their steps unmoved by it. When onlookers want to examine their feet, they consider this stupid. Why can't we be less materialistic, and look at the Power, they say.

Purification is a most important thing with them, and they will make no attempt until they have cleansed themselves physically and morally. More about this later. This Power, this electro-magnetism, this belief that they can walk on red-hot cinders, all is the magic anyone can do who **prepares** himself. That is the great thing. And belief.

So what do you do? You fill yourself with this Power by practising deep breathing, like the Fire Walkers, the Yogis, and the Tibetans. Do your deep breathing in the open air if possible, or by an open window. Oxygen possesses very considerable magnetic properties, and you must make good use of them. You cannot recharge your battery without. Shallow breathing actually breeds inefficiency of the mind. To bring out the magic in your mind a **full oxygen intake** must be a daily conscious habit. (Make a note of this in your diary book.)

There is an accident. What happens? Dozens of people seeming to come from nowhere, suddenly crowd around the poor, unfortunate victim. A voice echoes through the medley of men and women: 'Give 'im air! Give 'im air!'

Air, that magical 'something' which makes all the difference between life and death.

Unless you can help it, don't seek the petrol-laden air of the busy streets. There is the wonderful tonic air of the hill-tops. There is the salt-sea air of our lovely watering places, and you are lucky if you live within easy reach. Then there is the air-that-is-like-no-other of the sky. Fly in an open 'plane if you can get the chance, or join a gliding club. Climb a mountain if you are that way inclined, and get very high (you need not try for the top) where the air is very pure. The Great Psychologist was always taking Himself to the hills for long periods to reinforce Himself. Long periods.

Native air is of vast importance. If you can return to the place where you were born and practise deep breathing, you will soon realize that you feel much better breathing your native air. This is a fact. And because you are better, you can the more easily bring out the magic in your mind. You can think and act more clearly.

Have you ever thought about the air-crews? Their mental alertness soon drops when their oxygen-intake is affected. They have to be very oxygen-minded. It is essential to the lives of their passengers who depend upon their alertness for a safe journey. When flying over ten thousand feet they have to do something about it, or they would get mentally vague and could not do their job properly.

Regular deep breathing is a necessary thing towards making belief work. A Professor told me that we have seventy-two thousand nerve centres destined for the transmission of electro-magnetic forces. We only use about five thousand of them. Deep breathing helps us to use more. Think of the magic we could do if we cultivated the lot! And why not? These seventy-two thousand centres are not there for nothing.

Take deep breaths of this electro-magnetism; try it, live it, love it, become it. Don't worry about what it is, but use it.

This vital substance in which we live, move and have our being, can mean nothing to you unless you are aware of its enormous power, and make use of it to work magic.

Electricity is a substance and all and everybody is immersed in it. I breed tropical fish, but like the fishes who live in water and do not realize they are in water, so it is with humans. This substance is very delicate and most impression-able. Every time you think a thought it **registers**, and comes back to you according to the vibrations and wave lengths sent out from your mind. It was Emerson who said: 'Be careful what you set your heart on, for it will surely be yours,' and somebody else said, 'When a thinker is let loose on the planet, look out, for something is going to happen.'

There are materialists who will ridicule the idea that thoughts set up wave lengths, but remember what has been done with radar, and how radio waves go through brick walls, steel, and other so-called solid objects.

To give you a clearer idea of the radiation of thoughts, let us toss a pebble into the pond. You will see ripples or small waves. They spread out in circles and ultimately reach the shore, where they appear to stop. Two stones of different sizes and weights tossed in simultaneously at different places, will both set up ripples or waves converging on each other, and where the two stones meet there appears to be a struggle as to which is to overcome the other. The **larger** stone sweeps over the smaller, and creates waves in the wake of small ripples. The **bigger** your thought, the more forceful, the more vital will sweep over all the small thoughts and win through.

When we send a thought out into this substance in which we all live, it sets up waves, and the positive thought is much bigger, giving a quicker tempo, a far greater vibration.

Your positive thoughts sweep all aside as you plunge them into this ocean of electricity. They will sweep all over everything to reach their objective, because positive thoughts are like the biggest pebble, they have the higher wave.

What happens if you **believe?** That is a question that occurs to every mind in spite of the effort that some make to persuade themselves that nothing happens. At the De La Warr Laboratories, where they test out thought waves, they believe that a concentrated thought produces a pattern of that thought. A man sat in front of a special photographic apparatus and concentrated for two seconds on a penknife. This produced a perfect picture of the penknife which the man was thinking about. Then another man, who simply did not believe in this sort of thing, concentrated on the penknife for a photograph, but because there was disbelief, the film was a foggy mess, and no penknife was visible at all. They take these Thoughtographs with amazing results.

A photograph was taken of ordinary tap water, and then a photograph of water which had been blessed. The tap water film showed very thin radiations, but the blessed water had

SAN DIEGO COUNTY SHERIFF'S DEPARTMENT

CH	RX FREQ	TX FREQ	REPEATED	MONITORED BY CC	ASSIGNED USAGE
F–1	453.725	453.725	no	yes	Car to Car
F–2	453.750	458.750	yes	yes	North Coast
F–3	453.925	458.925	yes	yes	North Inland
F–4	453.500	458.500	yes	yes	East
F–5	453.950	458.950	yes	yes	South
F–6	453.400	458.400	yes	yes	Administrative (Office of Sheriff, Central Field Operations, Detention & Corrections, Office of Special Services, all Inspectors & all pagers)
F–7	453.575	458.575	yes	yes	Inquiry (10-21, 10-28, 10-29, CLETS, NCIC, etc.)
F–8	453.100	458.100	yes	yes	Emergency (UHF replacement for Blue)
F–9	453.425	458.425	yes	yes	North Tac
F–10	453.825	458.825	yes	no	South Tac
F–11	453.425	453.425	yes	no	North Tac/Cars
F–12	453.825	453.825	no	no	South Tac/Cars

TS 2/15 (6/82)

COMMUNICATIONS CENTER PHONE NUMBERS:

C.C. Emergency.................................. 911
C.C. Business.................................. 565-5200
C.C. Watch Commander.................. 565-5025
C.C. Sergeant.................................. 565-5030
Inquiry.. 565-5035
Sheriff's Records........................... 236-2971
TT/S.V.S.. 236-2969

General Phonetic Alphabet for Law Enforcement

A – ADAM	J – JOHN	S – SAM
B – BOY	K – KING	T – TOM
C – CHARLES	L – LINCOLN	U – UNIT
D – DAVID	M – MARY	V – VICTOR
E – EDWARD	N – NORA	W – WILLIAM
F – FRANK	O – OCEAN	X – X-RAY
G – GEORGE	P – PAUL	Y – YELLOW
H – HENRY	Q – QUEEN	Z – ZEBRA
I – IDA	R – ROBERT	

SAN DIEGO CO[UN]TY REGIONAL RADIO CODE

10-1	Receiving Poorly
10-2	Receiving Well
10-4	Acknowledgement
10-5	Relay
10-6	Busy
10-7	Out-of-Service
10-8	In-Service
10-9	Repeat
10-15	Remain in Service
10-16	Prisoner
10-18	Project Routine
10-19	Return to Station
10-20	Location
10-21	Phone Your Station
10-21H	Phone Your Home (Emergencies Only)
10-22	Disregard
10-23	Stand By
10-28	Vehicle Registration
10-29	Local Check for Wants Only (Persons or Plates)
10-29 NCIC	Check for All Wants
10-34	Are You Clear?
10-35	Dangerous Person Alert
10-36	Time Check
10-38	Meet the Officer 10-10
10-88	Request for Cover Unit
10-89	Bomb Threat
10-97	Arrived at Scene
10-98	Finished Last Assignment
11-6	Discharging Firearms
11-7	Prowler
11-8	Person Down
11-10	Conduct an Investigation
11-12	Injured Animal
11-13	Dead Animal
11-14	Dog Bite
11-15	Ball Game in Street
11-27	Felony Record - No Want
11-28	Misdemeanor Record - No Want
11-29	No Want
11-30	Incomplete Phone Call
11-31	Calling for Help
11-40	Notify If Ambulance Needed
11-41	Ambulance Needed
11-42	Ambulance Not Needed

11-25	Attempt Suicide
11-46	Report of Death
11-47	Injured Person
11-48	Furnish Transportation
11-49	Vehicle Stop - No License Check
11-50	Vehicle Stop - License Check (10-29 Only)
11-51	Pedestrian Stop/F.I.
11-52	Are You O.K.? (If response is other than Code 4 cover will be sent.)
11-53	Security Check
11-55	Hazardous or Chemical Spill
11-60	Investigate Water Leak
11-66	Signals Out of Order
11-71	Fire
11-80	Serious Injury Accident
11-81	Minor Injury Accident
11-82	Non-Injury Accident
11-83	No Detail Accident
11-84	Traffic Control
11-85	Request for Tow Truck
11-86	Special Detail
11-88	Citizen Assist
11-99	Officer Needs Help
187	Homicide
207	Kidnapping
211	Robbery
242	Battery
245	A.D.W.
246	Shooting At Dwelling
261	Rape
273a	Child Abuse or Neglect
288	Child Molest
314	Indecent Exposure
330	Gambling
415	Disturbance
417	Person with Weapon (Describe)
451	Arson
459	Burglary
470	Forgery
487	Grand Theft
488	Petty Theft
496	Possession of Stolen Property
537	Defrauding Innkeeper

594	Vandalism
597	Cruelty to Animals
602	Trespass
647f	Drunk
653m	Phone Threats
5150	Mental Case
10851	Auto Theft
10852	Tampering with Vehicle
11350	Possession of Dangerous Drugs
11357	Possession of Marijuana
12020	Carrying Concealed Weapon
12025	Possession of Illegal Weapon
20001	Hit and Run - Felony
20002	Hit and Run
23102	Reckless Driving
23103	Reckless Driving (Misdemeanor)
23152	Drunk Driving (Misdemeanor)
23153	Drunk Driving (Felony)
Code 3	Emergency (Lights and Siren)
Code 4	No Further Help Needed
Code 5	Stakeout
Code 6	Remain Clear of Area
Code 7	Eating
Code 8	Restroom
Code 9	Summer Uniform
Code 10	SWAT Alert
Code 11	SWAT Staging Location
Code 37	Subject Wanted
	M – misdemeanor
	F – felony
	T – traffic
Code Blue	Bus/Taxi in Trouble
Emergency	I Want the Air

DISPOSITION CODES

G.O.A.	Gone on Arrival
Q.O.A.	Quiet on Arrival
R.T.F.	Report to Follow
I.O.	Information Only
U.T.L.	Unable to Locate
	Will Cooperate
	Unfounded
	Checked OK

enormous radiations. So there is something in it, whether you like to believe it or not.

Our belief is to each one of us the most precious thing we have. People with little or no belief will try to lead you astray, and if you listen to them, you will be led to forget these truths and the memory of all this knowledge will fade away.

Some people expect 'luck' to be handed to them on a silver plate, without any effort on their part whatever.

You must learn to stand on your own mental and moral feet as an individual, and be able to say 'no' to the things you do not want to happen. You must rebel and say, **I will have no more of this kind of evil,** then it stops.

You do not believe me. Try it for yourself. Say, **I'll have no more of this from now on,** and lo, by the magic you have brought out of your mind, the trouble stops!

True, you may have to face adverse opinions and other little troubles, but if you stand firm and rebel against all that worries you, you will down the evil from the moment you decide to do it. Decision always magnetizes. When you decide to stop worrying, you start an immediate magnetic action which works for your good.

Never be afraid of 'they'. People are more afraid of 'they' than anything else in the world. Do not be afraid if you are laughed at. Take heart from the fact that sniggers made Epstein famous. When they laughed at one thing he did, he simply turned around and made – to their eyes – even more fantastic sculpture.

They laughed at Watt and the kettle lid. But Watt did not care. He **believed,** and got on with the job, and gave the world her locomotives.

They laughed at Marconi, even his own father laughed at him. He wanted him to throw up his ambitions and grow up as a country gentleman, and study music. But Marconi **believed** in himself, and preferred to experiment with electrical equipment in the attic. His father more than once threatened to throw it out of the window. Marconi cared nothing what the world thought, and became one of the greatest men since Christopher Columbus. He harnessed the ether to the service of man.

The Fords, the Edisons, the Marconis, and many others who have accomplished great things, all began with mind.

There is not, and never has been, an individual – a leader – who has not been laughed at. But do not be discouraged. Great people **believe**, in a positive way, and all the sniggering in the world cannot stop them working magic.

It is up to each one of us to ponder upon their belief, and backed by the memory of their spectacular courage, say unshakingly: **I can, and I will.**

Remember those wonderful words, 'And I, if I be lifted up from the earth, will draw all men to me.'

Your belief can bring out the magic in your mind. If people laugh at you and your super-optimism, know that it was exactly the same two thousand years ago.

'And he marvelled at their unbelief' (Mark 4. 2–6).

To recap, because I must be certain that you won't forget it, you are just so much electricity. And this electricity must be kindled as a fire in a stove, at first gently, until it springs of itself into a full glow.

You cannot buy this electricity in a bottle over the counter. It is a part of you which awaits development.

Water may save your life if you are thirsty, but it may also drown you. The same applies to electricity, as it will work magic beneficially employed, but it can cause death otherwise. **You must know how to use the power you possess,** and I am trying to tell you. The more electricity you develop, the stronger your belief and the more powerful do you become.

Mr Bryan Matthews, broadcasting from the BBC studio, London, in November 1930, demonstrated successfully that the human body **generates electric current** which can be led off from various parts of the body. He produced a 20th of a volt, amplified it, and rang a bell!

Consider for a moment. Charles R. Gibson, LL.D., F.R.S.E.,

says in his book **Modern Conceptions of Electricity,** 'Now that we know that every existing thing is composed of electricity. . . . Electricity attracts. . . . **We are made of electricity.**'

Without electricity you would not be. If your electricity 'took its flight' you would not be seen on this earth plane any more, because the body has no light of itself.

Every time you send out a destructive thought, you automatically separate yourself from your electricity, just as though you had pressed a button and the electric light had gone out. Negative thoughts of poverty, sickness, and limitation separate you from your electricity, and your light is obscured, because you have disconnected yourself. If you do it too often you will 'go out'. You will die.

You recharge your battery by using positive words and thinking positive thoughts.

Elizabeth Barrett, the poetess, was a cripple. She could not walk. What happened when she fell in love with Robert Browning, the poet? He was very determined that she **should** walk. He talked to her in a very positive way, and soon she **did** walk, from a distance right into his arms. And that was the beginning of a beautiful romance. She loved, she **believed**; two of the greatest forces were at work, and the magic came.

If you believe that you can lift your hand to your head you can do it easily, quickly, automatically. But if you **don't** believe that you can do it, your hand stays put, the magic will not work for a doubting mind. Never will it work with disbelief.

You may be confronted on all sides by appalling obstacles, disease, poverty, pain, fear, hatred. But you can overcome them all with belief.

'Our doubts are our traitors,' said Shakespeare. Has it ever occurred to you that you have for many years been a traitor to yourself?

If it is true (and it is) that all our doubts and negative thoughts hold us back from all we want, isn't it better to believe? A man who shows some determination is a man who has got **belief** in himself.

You have the power within you to make your world, your environment, **just what you want it to be.**

You can **create mentally** a new life for yourself; you can build a new world for yourself through visualization. Whatever you **believe** and **mentally create**, you can have. You can dissolve or overcome any obstacle. If obstacles are in the way of attainment, then you are not using the magic power within your mind.

Belief can carry you far. Belief can make you do the seemingly impossible, the fantastic – like I did.

It was when I went to entertain troops in the Middle East. At Tripoli I came upon a challenge. A gentleman came up to me and introduced himself as the Editor-Proprietor of the **Sunday Gibli** (the only Sunday paper there is in the English language).

He explained how he had read all the advance notices before I flew over from Malta, and admitted that he simply did not believe them.

So he outlined a challenge. In the office of the Chief of Police, there was a **sealed** and **taped** steel box. He would allow me to inspect the box, **and I was then to tell him what was inside.**

I went to the Chief of Police, who was a fine Egyptian character commanding respect. Locked in his safe was a box which, when produced, was found to be **tied** and **taped** up.

For a few moments I held the box silently in my hands.

'Well,' he pressed, **'what is in it?'**

'Let the box be brought to the theatre tonight,' I answered him. 'I am content, **I know what is inside.'**

So that night the box was brought with a Police escort to the theatre, and before the tapes and seals were cut, I stood before the footlights, and told the audience **I knew what was inside the box. It was a cheque.**

30

'It is for ten pounds,' I said. 'And it is made out to the Lord Mayor of London for the Flood Relief Fund.'

To their utter astonishment, when the box was opened, **there was the cheque!**

I drew hysterical praises, and was shaken warmly by the hand. The cheque was torn up, and another written out for double the amount.

This touch of magic in Tripoli caused a very real sensation, for Tripoli lies along the shore of the ancient seat of miracles and magic.

You, too, can bring out the magic in your mind.

3
The Magic Of Visualization

THE oldest story of visualization came from the very first Bibles. In these you will read that Jacob wanted to produce spotted cattle in order to be allowed to marry Rachel.

What did he do? He cut little round bits of bark off the trees, and laid these pieces of wood at the bottom of a clear stream where the cattle drank. Every time the beasts looked into the water, they visualized these spots, and their offspring brought Jacob his longed-for spotted cattle.

A more recent story of visualization came to light when Joseph Kennedy (a negro who went to his work repairing prams with only four shillings and sixpence in his pocket) began to visualize. By little instalments he bought a ticket in the Irish Sweepstake. He placed it in a Bible, and visualized every night that he would make a fortune. He visualized himself as coming into untold wealth. He could see this wealth coming to him. He had no shadow of doubt about it. He believed.

Then one day he paused to listen to the broadcast of the Derby, and when he heard that **Cameronian** had won and brought him a fortune of thirty thousand pounds, he slipped to his knees in front of the radio and solemnly gave thanks.

Visualization had brought out the magic in his mind, and he was now a rich man.

When you had only four and sixpence in your pocket, did you visualize?

The Great Psychologist said, 'Go and replenish', but look at the world, look at the hospitals, that is how man has replenished. And all because he has never been taught that he is his own creator. Every time you use your mind you create. You produce a mental picture that immediately takes form. Like the man who visualized the penknife at the De La Warr Laboratories. Are you visualizing intensely, or is all you are getting a foggy mess?

One of the quickest ways to bring out the magic in your mind, and to obtain anything you set your heart on, is to practise **visualizing** what you want. Nothing but good can come from visualization if you are positive in your desires. The things you want will come automatically. As you progress you will find a **gradual transformation** taking place in your life.

When you are out on a sunny day and you see a stream of cars going by, do you begin to say to yourself, 'How on earth do they get those beautiful cars?' You haven't seen a really old one pass by.

Well, **you** can have a luxurious car. You are entitled to one. What's to do about it?

If you really want a car, and you command your subconscious positively, you can get it, for the subconscious can do anything you want it to do, within the confines of the material plane.

The first step is knowing what you want. Exactly what and when. You want a car, but do you want an old Austin or a brand new Cadillac? Perhaps it's a Jaguar you want? Be specific, tell your subconscious in so many words, exactly the make and type of car you want. And when you want it. The new Jaguar isn't going to do you much good when you are on your deathbed. Make it clear what you want and when.

You wouldn't ask for a new Jaguar in five minutes, because your intellect would say, 'There's no hope of me getting such a car in five minutes!' and you wouldn't get it. Be reasonable. Give a sensible time limit. Now the thing is, you may be absolutely unable to see how on earth you could get a new Jaguar on what you are earning at the moment, but other factors come into play. You may get a sudden windfall. You may hit the Jackpot in some exciting competition. If you do the pools, possibly it's your turn for the big money. Don't draw lines between the possible and the impossible. Leave it to your subconscious to get it for you in its own magic way, by command of your will.

You do not know where you can get it from? You do not know where you can put it when you get it? You don't know how you can afford to run it? Oh, ye of little faith, do not worry about that. That is entirely your subconscious mind's business. That is what your subconscious is for; to look after you; to answer your problems. Never for one moment should you limit yourself because you cannot see where such a glorious thing is coming from. Go and look at the cars, especially the Jaguars (if that is what you want) and **feel** joy in your heart. Feeling counts. Feeling is the secret. When it comes to control of the subconscious mind, feeling plays a very important part. Feel that you can get a Jaguar car when you want it. You are going to enjoy life when you get it, **feel** that excitement now. **You obtain your desire by feeling as if you had already got what you want now.**

See yourself at the wheel. See yourself driving that wonderful automobile. See it draw up in front of your house. If you do this; if you see that picture, it is bound to materialize. It is the law.

Screwy, that's what he is. Screwy.

No, friend. To create through the magic of visualization, you must hold the picture clearly in your mind. Every detail of it. Better still, get yourself a scrap book, and paste in pictures of the things you want. Put that Jaguar on the first page. You think it's all nonsense, this visualization? Right, you've hit it on the head with a hammer. It may be called nonsense, but it may none the less be true.

'For lack of vision, my people perish.' How foolish not to believe. What did Arnold Wesker make his character say in 'I'm talking about Jerusalem'?

Dave: Don't moan at me about visions. Don't you know they don't work? You child you – visions don't work!

Ronnie: They do work. And even if they don't work then for God's sake let's try and behave as though they do – or else nothing will work.

See what I mean? You have got to see the thing you want in your mind's eye, and know that through the power of all creation (the power of your magic) it is coming. Behave as though you believe.

If it is a house you want, you have got to see a mental picture. You must see the house, the furniture, the curtains, the cushions, the vase of flowers on the table. You know exactly the sort of house you want, and you must see it in every glorious detail. **And behave as though you had already got it.** Go and buy something for it, however small and inexpensive, but buy something if it's only a vase to put the flowers in, or a shovel for the fire, or a duster. Any little thing will do, just to 'make believe'. As Arnold Wesker says, for God's sake behave as though it works – or else nothing will happen.

It is the wisdom of the Tibetans. It is what the saints and sages of the past have studied all their lives. It is no new experiment. It is not merely untried theory. Visualize. See pictures. Look at your scrap book every day, and **believe.**

When some people do not get what they want quickly, they kid themselves it is all for the best that they should not have it. This is a paralysing thought.

Perhaps they aren't as keen to do things off their own bat as they used to be. Tele-viewing has made people lazy; it has made people lose their initiative. They are content to make do. They no longer **feel**. All those exciting people on the screen feel for them.

This is negative and cowardly. There is no rhyme nor reason in it. It is like waiting for the end; like as though you thought there was nothing to live for.

Such people stagnate and have a dull, monotonous life. They miss all the luxuries they could so easily have with right thinking. You must want a thing so intensely, so fiercely, that you **feel** you cannot live without it. You can ask your subconscious and you can get it if you visualize. I don't care whether it's wealth or health. I do not care whether it's a washing machine or a record player. You can ask your subconscious and if you 'see' it and believe it, you can get it.

Grasp this fact – this tremendous fact – that by observing the basic rules of magic, you can step into spectacular success and be happier than you have ever dreamed possible. Your thoughts and words are all-powerful, but the most powerful thing of all is **emotion**. What you **see** for yourself. What you **feel**. Feeling is in the heart. Your whole heart must be in getting this thing you want, or it is useless to go on. You cannot make magic and all you wish it to bring you, a mathematical certainty, unless there is strong **feeling**. There is no haphazard road to the attainment of your desires. Anyone who tells you there is, is leading you down a blind alley. You must, as you visualize, **feel** your desires will be met, so that your subconscious is driven irresistibly to secure these things for you. It is not what you do once in a while, but what you do habitually every day, that counts.

Seeing and **Feeling** are necessities.

The ancient Greeks were undoubtedly some of the best exponents of visualization. They were very conscious of the sense of **seeing**, and much of their radiant health and beauty may be attributed to it. When a Grecian woman was expecting a child, statues of Venus and Apollo were put in her room in the knowledge that the constant mental vision would react upon her physical condition, and give her child the beauty of one or the other of these divinities.

Pause now, and reflect on the importance of visualization. Dedicate your whole heart to it! Be in earnest! Practise it each day with exhilarating joy. Be a super-optimist and have a daring imagination. You could draw a Rolls-Royce from Africa if you wanted to.

Hold but one pessimistic thought and you will be cut off from the magic you are seeking. Cultivate a strong belief, be absolutely positive, and you will release this wonderful magic power. Be an optimist par excellence.

Visualize at night before retiring. Visualize as you lie in bed. Don't think of failure. If an obstacle looms up, remember Herbert Casson, who said: 'In a vision I saw a brave man walking briskly, with his head up, on a rough and twisting path. As I watched him, he gave a shout of joy.

' "Hurrah!" he said. "Cheerio! I see another obstacle!" '

Obstacles were as nothing to him. He dismissed them. He laughed at them.

Visualize whenever you are alone and quiet, and in your 'retreat' room, the little study you made for yourself. You will be guided to a new and wonderful experience.

You must repeat over and over again the name of the things you want. Repetition is essential. Tap, tap, tap on your mind. Name it. See it. And tell your subconscious to get it for you. What may appear as coincidences are simply the working out of the pattern which you started with your weaving.

There was a woman who wanted a piano. She took to test the power of visualization. She did not visualize money with which to buy it, because if she came into money she knew her husband would be annoyed if she spent it on a piano when they were so in need of other things. So she visualized a piano. She made a place in her drawing-room, and every day when she dusted the furniture, she would 'pretend', just for fun, to dust her imaginary piano. She was thrilled and gloriously excited. (The **feeling** I was telling you about.) She put

37

plenty of feeling into the situation. To her, the piano would drop from the skies any day now.

After four weeks, a traveller called and asked her if she wanted a piano. He said when he passed the house he had the idea that somebody wanted a piano. She laughed and said she did, but she had to let him go because she had no money.

Then another piano merchant called a few days following this, and she said to herself joyfully, 'It must be working. These piano men calling on me like this is a sign that my thoughts in the air are taking effect.' She grew more and more thrilled, and worked herself up into great excitement. She sang as she did the chores. Life was wonderful. Wonderful. Every single day she visualized the piano in the drawing-room.

She stood up one day in a crowded bus to give her seat to an old lady. They got off the bus together at the same stopping place. They did not know each other, so did not speak. But the old lady dropped her umbrella, and the other picked it up, and like that they got chatting.

Here it is. The old lady said: 'I suppose you don't happen to know anyone who would store a piano, do you? We have got to live abroad for a while, and I want to let someone use it for three years in lieu of storage.'

The one who had been visualizing the piano was like one spellbound. The law had worked. She got a wonderful piano – for nothing – and at the end of three years when the old lady came to reclaim it, through the power of this same visualization she had become rich and was well able to buy herself a new one.

If her consciousness had been bigger, she could have had her own new one in the beginning. She realized this later, of course. It was the measure of her bucket. If you want a quart instead of a pint, you have got to enlarge your bucket. If you want a larger salary, you have got to see your pay envelope bulging out. You have got to see it in your mind's eye before it will operate in the objective.

The piano woman conceived the idea that she could store

somebody's piano. By the law of attraction the other woman came across her path and made this possible. It would have been greater if she had realized that there are millions of pianos all over the world, and that she could easily have had a brand new one. She got what she wanted.

You must wait patiently while the subconscious is assimilating your desires, and goes about it in **its own way** to bring these things to you. Suddenly, the things you command come as if out of the blue, or you will be guided in which way to attain them, and the correct course of action will be indicated. You must follow this course **immediately and unquestionably.** There must be no hesitation on your part, for the subconscious is **always right.** There must be no mental reservation, no deliberation whatever. You must act at once. Only by so doing will you make the subconscious serve you whenever you want it to. Obediently perform the seemingly irrelevant things, then soon you will find the thing is yours! Magic.

Then, when you look back, you will see that the things you were called upon to do (by the subconscious) all formed the **logical line of events,** the last one of which is the reward of your dearest dream.

There was a man who fell in love with a girl and he wanted to marry her, but she seemed more fond of someone else. Did he give up in despair? No. He continually visualized himself going up to that girl, and placing a ring upon her finger, and the day came along when that mental picture was shown on the screen of his life. His wildest dream came true through this power which brings magic.

'That is my best hat, I won't wear it today,' and 'This is my best suit, I must not put that on now.'

Why not? Because you are limiting yourself, and you are thinking that it will be soiled and wear out, and you cannot have another one yet awhile. If you could actually **see** – if you could **visualize** where another hat is coming from next week or in a fortnight's time, you would dress in all your glory today, and be happy about it

But you cannot see. That is the pity of it. You lack vision.

Wear your best clothes now and know that you are going to get plenty more new things – very soon. Know what sort you want, the colour, the texture. Visualize it in your head. Before you know where you are you will get it! It will be yours. How? That is the business of your subconscious. It is not for you to worry. When a destructive thought creeps in telling you what a fool you are, that all this is nonsense, say quickly, 'Get out of here, you old tempter you. You are not going to find a place in my mind.' When you see your wallet as flat as though an elephant had sat on it – that is the tempter. You are seeing double. You are seeing bad. You are seeing a lie. Speak with authority and say, 'Get thou behind me. Get out of here.' Blessed is emptiness for it shall be filled. See it filled.

It is visualization that creates through the power of mind. Every poor condition has been brought on this way. You had to conceive the idea or it never would have been. You had to see yourself poor, and think of yourself as being poor, or you never would have been poor. You had to speak of poverty, or you never would have been empty-handed. The subconscious creates what you give it. If your idea is poverty and you think poverty, then you cannot work magic. No power on earth can make you rich if you hold such thoughts. And through the law of attraction you draw all others in the same miserable condition.

Is it worth it, all these depressed conditions, for the sake of thinking wrongly? Because you will play the silly game your friends and neighbours are playing. Is it not just as easy to think 'I am rich'? It takes no more energy, no more time to think like that – and look at the difference. Look what you get. You get riches, by the magic in your mind.

You have got to know what you want. What do you want in this world? Most people have no real idea what they want. They are like children in a toy shop, who clutch first at one thing and then drop it for another with brighter and more alluring colours, and throw that away for something else until, at long last, they come empty-handed out of the shop. Then they blame Fate when they ought to be blaming themselves. You must know exactly what you want.

See it in your mind's eye, exactly the thing you need. Think of it constantly. Say the word. Then all you have got to do is to watch it turn up, by magic.

If you invite better conditions they are bound to come. You do not have to think things are impossible. You have to think that better days are on the way. Better days simply are on the way, if you command your subconscious positively.

And be grateful. Be grateful for what you already have. Don't resent anything, don't be peeved if life is not just as you want it. Gratitude for what you already have is important. Bless your present condition. When you have conquered your environment, when you have not dropped your hat and run, then life will be a grand sweet song, and magic will manifest quickly. Decide to be courageous. Cultivate a tolerance, a quietness, a sort of sparkling expectedness about things. This is the way you should live, if you want to bring magic into your life. It is very easy for us to think we can get along on our own, that meditation is not necessary, that it is enough just to repeat what you want. We may for a short time be able to run under our own steam, but eventually we slow down, form negative habits, become aged and alone, and no better, no richer, than we were years ago. Meditation, listening-in and speaking to your subconscious, is more than a two-way conversation. It establishes a magnetic power line between you and your subconscious, gives energy, and provides your dearest needs. You shouldn't have to wait for poverty and disaster to open yourself up to this wonderful line of communication, it should be a part of your life – every day – whatever conditions you live under, unhappy or happy.

Take your wants on to another dimension. Be happy. Magic cannot pierce a fog. You must be bright, show enthusiasm, a feeling of expectancy. If you think it is impossible to get what you want, you automatically weaken the power, and you weaken what you already possess. The Bible refers to this when it says, 'Even that which they have shall be taken away.' It is strange, but it is true. And it should be underlined ten times!

You must accept what you already have with gratitude. Think and work with a song in your heart. A child sees no difficulty in magic; a child has no difficulty whatever in visualizing. He will put a box over his head, with holes in it for eyes and mouth, and he sees himself as a Spaceman! A soap-box on wheels becomes a racing car as he speeds along the road. It is only when we grow up that we lose this enlightenment, this acceptance of the impossible.

'Unless you become as a little child. . . .' Isn't that what we are meant to do?

You may live in a caravan, but you are irritable when you have to go and draw water a little way up the field, when you have to shop for food and carry heavy parcels, when you have to get in more coal for the fire. You do not accept the path you are on, and if you keep on resenting things, you will cloud out all magnetic power to work magic. You must raise your thinking to a higher dimension; you must be grateful, or magic has no power to manifest. You don't need to bother whether you have much money or not, whether you are rich or poor, whether your body aches all over or whether it doesn't. Do away with this smallness of mind, all this littleness of living, and realize that you are on your way to a higher dimension right now. That is all that matters, in the world of making magic.

Enter a very deep and rich silence and whatever you possess at the moment, accept it whole-heartedly. Give thanks. Once you accept it, the condition will commence to change for the better, because you will be reaching out to higher dimensions than the one in which you now live. How can your subconscious communicate when your mind is so turbulently ungrateful? Put yourself in a state of magnetic power. Every moment you live in gratitude, you are actually becoming a fourth-dimensional being, and once this begins to operate, magic takes place.

This is exciting. This is how you should always feel. Remember, you can go through life adoring, accepting, approving, enjoying – or you can go through life perpetually grumbling! Get rid of ingratitude and resentment, then magic will flow.

Tell yourself that nothing in the world will stop you. It is necessary to tell yourself this, and believe it. You see, the sooner your subconscious gets the idea that you want to change, the better, and the sooner your desires begin to take form. Hold the picture in your mind's eye. Visualize yourself as being grateful and happy. The mirror technique can do this. Look at yourself in the mirror as you command your sub-conscious. See yourself as a smiling, grateful person. The mirror technique intensifies your thoughts. Thousands of years ago men talked to their mirrored face in a pool of water.

Where before you could lose your temper and it didn't matter very much, now it **does** begin to matter. You are wanting to work magic, and you are wanting to reach the fourth-dimension when magic becomes a reality. You must intensify your drawing power, and you can only do this by purification; by loving instead of hating, by not losing your temper, by unselfishness, by meditation, by giving.

You must discipline your lower self, and you must not now think some of the things you used to think. You must withdraw from life to a certain extent, as you once knew it, be 'in the world but not of it'. You must concern yourself with things of the mind, and strive for perfection of behaviour, so that you can raise the mind at will, to a higher dimension. Do not be too locked in the physical body, because like this you 'block' your channels of abundance. If you don't visualize what you want, you are merely holding on to old negative beliefs, old might-not-get ideas which kill any chance of magic. When you start to worry whether you will get that car or not (or whatever it is you are visualizing) you 'block' your channel. Let your subconscious work, and the best way is to stop worrying, stop caring; to get, you have got to forget. As soon as you cease anxious caring, you open the way for your subconscious to work magic. As you think, so does your subconscious work. By living a life of resentment, ingratitude, dissatisfaction, jealousy, and so on, your aura becomes denser and denser until there is a blockage. You can no longer attract.

When you catch yourself thinking negative thoughts, immediately talk to yourself. You are destroying your body. You are emptying your purse. Raise yourself up from the dead; from dead thoughts, dead ideas, and ask your subconscious to forgive you for misappropriating its wonderful power. You have the power within you to work magic, but you automatically shut yourself off from this power because you are lukewarm; you are asleep at the switch. You are out of your kingdom. You have deliberately thrown yourself out. Every single moment you are choosing what you are going to be. If you serve sickness you are going to be ill. If you serve poverty you are going to be poor. If you serve health you are going to be well. If you serve riches you are going to be wealthy. If you serve only the physical, you will never get to the other departments of your mind, you will never reach the fourth-dimension, the mind that works magic, for while serving only the physical you are bound to the law of cause and effect. For everything you do which is not right you will have to suffer, because that is the law. Violation of the law causes misery and suffering, and that is why we have other planes of thought, so that we can choose and be free. You have got to go beyond the human consciousness to know the way to work magic.

People who say they are poor are ill. Downright ill. They might as well dig a hole in the back garden and get in it, for they are dead already. They go on struggling and struggling, and grumbling and grumbling. There is a deal too much of it going on in the world, and I expect there were such people present at the Miracle of the Loaves and Fishes, who complained that the bread was stale and the fish not very nice.

Accept what you have to eat and drink, with gratitude. Accept your environment and how you have to live. Visualize the better things you would like to eat and drink, and visualize the wine on the table. Visualize a nice new home and all the luxuries you want to put in it. Visualize the Jaguar, the motor yacht, everything you desire, but don't complain. Don't ever complain. This is the thing that will stop you getting it. Before any magician works magic, he says Abracadabra (Speak the Blessing). Bless every condition you are in, bless what you already have, then you can work magic.

Do I visualize? Of course I do. Before every performance I visualize people hailing taxis, leaping on buses, getting their car out of the garage, all speeding their way to the theatre where I am to appear. I 'see' people ringing up to book seats, a queue at the booking office, everywhere, people, people, people, all coming to my show. I always play to packed houses; I believe that what I see for myself, I get.

And in like fashion I 'see' people falling over each other in the foyer, waiting to buy this book. I 'see' them going into the bookshops, picking it up off the counter, and handing over their money at the cash desk. I 'see' them sending to my publisher for a copy. Everywhere I look (in my mind's eye) I see people clamouring to read what I've written, and then coming to see my performance not once, but again and again.

Certainly, I visualize. Wouldn't you?

4
Power Of The Subconscious

BRINGING out the magic in your mind works on the same principle as stage magic. It is that which is **underneath** that makes it work.

Suppose I take a silk top hat. I hold the brim in my hands, and the silk top below hides something. I pass my hand over the upturned brim, smile, and say **Abracadabra**. The next moment I draw out a white rabbit, coloured silk handker-chiefs, or perhaps, a dove. The magic comes from **underneath**.

It is very important to remember this. It is the same with your subconscious mind, that is underneath your conscious mind, and it knows the past, present, and future.

The subconscious mind is that wonderful part of your mind which regulates the beating of your heart, the breathing of your lungs, and all the processes of digestion and assimilation. The conscious mind is that mind you use every day and with which you think and speak. It is non-creative and takes its life from the subconscious. It is but a mimic.

It is the **underneath** mind (your subconscious) that brings out the magic, and you must have a constant **awareness** of this. You must never forget it. The best way to bring this **awareness** up to scratch is to cultivate the habit of dictating to it. Tell it things. The subconscious acts on your commands.

It keeps a faithful record of all you have said, felt, and done in your life. The limits of its power are unknown. It never sleeps and it comes to your support in time of great trouble, and aids you to do that which seems impossible. When properly employed it can work.

Fakirs and Yogis make use of the subconscious to gain their extraordinary control over bodily functions. They can sit naked in deep snow and keep warm. They do astounding things and have complete mastery over physical resources.

What is the power? It is the subconscious.

Yogis can lash their bodies with a strong whip but no blood comes. Such is the power of their underneath mind.

The aboriginal sleeps with his death bone under his head to impress his subconscious. Like that he can do black magic. The Westerner writes his wish on a piece of paper and slips it under his pillow that he may sleep on it, and that impresses his subconscious, who acts upon his wish. Fire Walkers take hundreds of pieces of paper on which their wishes are written, and put them into the fire before walking upon it. A famous Swedish actress of film and television admits that when she has difficulty in learning a script, she puts the script under her pillow at night – and knows the lines perfectly next morning!

Give **commands** to your subconscious. The subconscious never fails to obey any order commanded, if the order is clear and emphatic, and given with **feeling**. The stronger you **feel** about something, the quicker it is going to happen.

A terrible snowdrift in Britain reveals the truth of this. A man, stranded in his car waiting to be rescued, was cold and dying. A young woman came along and talked to the man's subconscious mind for hour after hour, while her husband flashed S.O.S. signals on the headlamps of his Rolls-Royce in the Woodhead Pass in Yorkshire.

They had seen the man get out of his car, try to walk along the road, and collapse in the snow from a heart attack. They brought him to their car, put coats over him, and made their

47

dog lie on him to keep him warm. At 3 a.m. he said quietly, 'I'm going to die' and he collapsed again.

Then the woman began to talk to his subconscious constantly. She kept whispering close to him, 'You must stay alive. You must stay alive. You must **stay alive.**'

At noon they hauled the sick man to an inn, and still the young wife kept repeating softly, the same words, **You must stay alive.** This is how Rodney Prickett of Timperley, Cheshire, was saved. By the magic of his subconscious.

Some little while ago the newspapers carried a story of Mrs Glover of Clapham. She had been talking to the subconscious mind of her seven-year-old son Paul for eight months. Like this she completely cured his asthma. And *The Lancet* recently told of a similar story. Repetition to the subconscious is like the chuff-chuff of the locomotive that takes a train across the country. If it is a love of poetry the mother wants for her baby, repetition of poetry said softly, slowly, acts upon the sleeping child's mind, and what goes in, comes out, sooner or later.

A mother can give her child a love of good music by playing a record-player softly beside a sleeping child. She would play the sort of music she wanted the child to grow up to be fond of. I used health repetitions on myself when I was in hospital.

The conscious part of the mind is said to constitute less than a tenth of the whole of it. It is the subconscious that works while we sleep and during our waking hours. In the case of a baby who is far too young to understand that he or she has a mind at all, the mother or father can do a lot. And the action of one mind upon another **at a distance** is no more extraordinary than the action of the magnet on iron or the influence of the moon on the sea.

At a festival the Indians staged in South Africa, one Indian (the principal figure at the festival) was jabbed with skewers, large needles, and pins through his cheeks Large things like fish-hooks were jabbed into his back. He was given a pair of nail clogs to walk on. Many others had skewers jabbed into their flesh, but none showed signs of pain or blood. It is well known that bleeding can be controlled by the subconscious mind. Sometimes hypnotists demonstrate this fact by piercing through their hand with a hat pin, without any trace of bleeding whatever. Rasputin controlled the bleeding of a sick boy by giving commands to his subconscious. The boy was the son of the Czarina of Russia. Doctors had failed to control the bleeding, but the subconscious worked the magic at once!

Ask your subconscious to awaken you at 5 a.m. and you will awaken on the stroke! I have done this many times when I have had to make an early journey somewhere.

When Leonardo da Vinci, who was not only a great artist but a great engineer and scientist, found himself at a standstill from lack of sufficient serviceable ideas, he would stare at a heap of ashes. Like this he would pass into a profound state of self-hypnosis, and in this condition there would arise in his mind just the ideas he wanted. These ideas would be uprushes from his subconscious. In effect, until da Vinci enlisted the aid of his subconscious mind he remained a man of talent, that was all.

It is possible to give yourself valuable suggestions, and through the power of the subconscious alter, perhaps, your whole attitude to life, turn sadness into joy, and melancholy into **joie de vivre**.

It is possible to put yourself into the somnambulistic state (discovered by the Marquis Armond de Puysegur, who was a pupil of Anton Mesmer) and tell yourself that you will perform a certain action at a certain time, and you will do so faithfully.

The subconscious mind can acquire knowledge of conditions relating to anything.

Have you a problem? Put it to your subconscious and wait patiently while it assimilates your worries, and then it goes about its own way to work it out for you. In due course, with the flowing of ideas and plans, a solution to your problem will be revealed to you, and the correct course of action indicated. You must follow this course immediately up to the last detail.

Look at the people who tell you your fortune in cups, with cards or crystal ball, and the people who read your hands. They will say brightly, 'I see a dark woman coming to your home with a large package . . . oh, such a large package it is. She is coming to your home in two or three days. And I see a letter for you, with money in it.'

'Oh, is that so?' you say and you begin to prick up your ears. A letter. One that is going to contain money. You are not expecting it, but anyway, **it is coming,** and you think, 'Why, who is sending it? Who can it be coming from?'

You do not know. Why? Because you are asleep at the switch. Your trolley is off the wire. You are not alive to the magic that can be brought out of your mind. Of course there is a letter on the way with money in it (if you believe) and not let the thought go.

Maybe a horoscope says you will have **immense changes** this year, exciting good news, sudden and dramatic money and travel are indicated. Believe it. Never mind whether you can see any exciting changes or not, believe and it will come to pass. You can make these predictions come true.

Your subconscious which knows your past, present, and future (I have said this before) can warn you of danger. I had a premonition. I remarked to my manager one evening that I had a 'feeling' that this was my unlucky night. We were making a journey in my car from the North of England, and because I had this 'feeling' (my subconscious was warning me) I had an 'awareness' and drove my car at very slow speeds that saved us both from certain death. My car was smashed, but the warning made me drive slowly, which consequently saved our lives.

Some people attribute a thing like this to mere chance. I was just lucky, they say, refusing to acknowledge that I had been warned and acted accordingly by driving slow. These are the people who never believe anything, and the world is full of them. My hobby is driving a fast sports car at night, and I have a positive premonition that I will not be involved in an accident. I take no risks that will involve others, although I am convinced of this in my own mind. It is a hunch I have got, and where do these hunches come from? The subconscious. It is the subconscious that impresses you. I never make any mistake when something inside of me tells me what to do.

You can always distinguish a hunch or the voice within from wishful thinking. When you practise meditation daily you soon begin to recognize a hunch. This difference in feeling cannot possibly be put in words, but you will recognize it at once, you will not be carried away with the wrong ideas. When something impresses you, **you know**. It is something you cannot explain. People often say, 'Something told me to do . . .' or 'Something told me not to do . . .' These are hunches. You do not actually hear a voice, but you are conscious that something is being said to you, and that you must follow it. Perhaps, like many other people, you do not think that you are responsible for what happens in your life. But you are. Had you listened to your subconscious every day in the quiet of meditation, you would have been warned about so much, and helped a great deal. You have had no direction, no guidance. But the past is gone. Forget it for the moment. When you have become well acquainted with all this that I am telling you, you can use your past profitably, not with regrets.

Let me tell you what the **Sunday Graphic** had to say about me in their issue **May 2nd, 1954.**

'**Ten million people in Britain who saw the Mystery of the Bottle on television last week are still asking themselves: was this the biggest stunt or the most successful hunch in history?**

And 36-year-old Al Koran, the man who forecast the

51

result of the Two Thousand Guineas on TV last Sunday – four days before the race – was the first to admit, when I met him last week, that it is a fair question.

As long as you're baffled – and who wasn't? – Koran is happy. And this small, highly strung, prematurely grey man swears it was a hunch.

Note that. A hunch. And they go on to say:

Then why did he not collect the packet of all time by backing his fancy with a bookmaker? He has an answer to that one, too. You see, he had another hunch that if he did, the forecast would not come off.

Now, Mr Koran, please come off it. One hunch I can take, but a second hunch about the first hunch, please!'

You see the sort of thing you are up against when you start to talk about hunches to people? How could I explain all that I have said so far in this book, in a nutshell? I couldn't. All I know is that I must act on my hunches. You must act on a hunch that your subconscious gives you, because the subconscious is always right. The second hunch was like a reminder that, if you back a horse you know is going to be a winner, you are not being fair to the other fellow who has not this knowledge. In other words, you are **cheating**. I have a great respect for my power. I do not stoop to cheating, and I know if I did it would simply boomerang on me, and cut off my power to work magic any more. But you can't explain all this to a press group eager to trap you if they can. Where does the **purity** come in, if I start cheating? Only a fool would want to lose the tremendous power that I am blessed with, and that you will be blessed with if you don't cheat, but play the game.

So I act on my hunches. As I have said before, you must not question your subconscious about the whys and wherefores as to how it gets you this or that. You must **believe** unquestionably, and act on it.

Another paper said of me:

'Remember Al Koran the magician who produced the

certified £5 note with a forecast of the Guineas' winners on
it a few weeks back? Believe it or not, before his appearance
in "What's My Line?" and "Quite Contrary" he was calling
on theatrical agents and having doors slammed in his face.
But afterwards the same agents were ringing him up and
asking him to accept fabulously high rates to do the same act
they had refused on cheaper terms a few days previously.

"... the truth is, it was a hunch. ... I just backed everything on my hunch." '

And the paper goes on to say that I was once a hairdresser.
My psychological powers have brought me fame and fortune,
and I have no wish to turn back the clock. If you act on your
hunches, there is no limit to where you will get. Success will
come in leaps and bounds, if you do not use your power to
outdo the other fellow; to cheat. But however successful you
become, don't expect people to praise you or believe you.
Some will, of course, but there are always people who are
envious, jealous, and critical. Never mind, go on loving them.
You may remember the famous picture. In this picture Love
was depicted as a woman sitting on top of the world, with a
bandage across her eyes. Love has to be blind. When you are
on top of the world, remember that picture, and turn a blind
eye to those who envy and are jealous of you.

The Sunday Pictorial on May 2nd, 1954, had the headlines
Al Koran was tricking you.

'... If any of you still believe that Al Koran has psychic
powers because he appeared to bring off a big racing "forecast" you have been taken for a ride. ...'

Makes you laugh, doesn't it? There are people who can't
be bothered to study psychology themselves; to give years and
years to the study of it, as I have done. All the way along the
line you will find people having a dig at you, the moment
magic appears on your horizon. Even the Master Magician
who turned water into wine suffered this. His own people
turned against Him. As soon as you begin to get criticism,
and people turn green with envy, over your new car, your

diamonds, and all that – you will know what to expect. It's a sign that you're doing fine, so like the lady sitting on top of the world, shut your eyes to all this nonsense and carry on, victory after victory, to the top.

Perhaps in your young days you read Hans Andersen's story, **What the old man says is always right.** I want to remind you, **that what the subconscious mind says is always right.**

The mind is very wonderful, and the study of it is more wonderful still, because you come to realize step by step as you begin to piece everything together, that magic is the outcome if you play your cards right. Every day of your life you can be working some magic for yourself, and for others around you. Your castles won't tumble if you bank on your subconscious mind.

From the **Daily Express**, Saturday, August 25th, 1951:

'It was certainly mystifying: this business of the Daily Express headline that Al Koran, the 34-year-old mind-reader, said he would predict four days before the news.

It started last Monday when Koran said he would write down Saturday's main headline. The news Editor gave him a piece of office notepaper signed by several members of the staff.

Koran wrote on it, folded it, had the outside countersigned and put it in a small tin.

The tin was sealed, wrapped in ribbon, and put in a jar. The jar went into a sealed cardboard container, and the whole thing was locked up in the Daily Express office.

On Saturday night I took it to the London Society of Magicians' annual show. I opened the container and jar; took out the tin.

Koran whipped it from my hand to hold it up to the audience for a few seconds; then handed it back for me to open.

Inside the tin I found this headline prediction:

OIL – TROOPS RECEIVE ORDERS.

Remember the main headline in Saturday's Daily Express?

It was:

OIL – TROOPS GET ORDERS.

The countersigned notepaper was the same. The container had not been tampered with.

Says Koran: I simply followed a hunch.

And me, Ladies and gentlemen – I simply give up! '

Follow your hunches and you will never go wrong.

5
Silence And Meditation

STILLNESS is one of the most important attributes to bring out the magic in your mind. There is chaos and confusion in the world today. This mad state of affairs, together with the perpetual struggle for existence, we call **living**. It is not living.

The world is too much with us. Most people are living at a break-neck pace, and their days and nights are crowded with things to be done, or things they want to do. **Aloneness** is often very difficult to procure, and many would feel unhappy if they had it. Yet, if you are to bring out the magic in your mind, you must, above all things, cultivate silence and meditation.

What is meditation? It is the practice of **mindfulness**, attentiveness, awareness; it establishes an attitude of mind.

In the stress and strain of life today, with sputniks and atom-bombs rending the air, loud-speakers tearing our ears, and a lot of other sounds, the voice of your subconscious goes unnoticed.

Some of us cannot bear silence or being alone more than a few minutes. This attitude must be broken down at once. The deep silence of a quiet place is something most of us have never known. How, then, can we hear the voice of our subconscious mind? We cannot.

A quiet place is essential, and if you have not got one, you must remake your world. The task is nothing less than that. Noise saps your energy. Noise kills any chance of you being a magician.

All of us at some time or another have been nearly driven 'mad' by noise. The noise of cars revving up, radios blaring, a dog barking on and on, the noise of aeroplanes hour after hour, juke boxes in every other café you go into. Always a background of noise.

The greatest people avoid from time to time the society of men and women. They get right away, either in a room of their own and lock the door, or they walk up a hill where they can sit and quietly meditate.

Make yourself a study 'away from it all', even though it's only an attic room. Go to this 'retreat' regularly. Or if you cannot do this, go high up on some hill where you can sit alone. You must dwell alone with yourself for a little while every day.

You must shut out all noises, and listen to the voice of your subconscious – the voice of magic. You must always take that 'listening' attitude, as though you were expecting to hear. You cannot go into the silence as long as you are thinking about the world. You must **silence** your thoughts. Empty your mind.

You have allowed thoughts to come into your mind at any moment, and any kind of thought, and you have to learn to control your mind. This is important. You have got to shut your mind to outside things.

Every day you must work with it until you can sit in the silence for at least half an hour. Go into the silence – and **listen** – every day until you can sit like that for one hour or better still, two.

You must develop your sixth sense like this. You are guided by your reasoning faculties, you have to reason things out, but if you would listen to the voice of your subconscious, **and pay attention to it,** you would be right every time.

You may reason things out, but they will never turn out as you think they will. It will not come right that way at all. Ask your subconscious to guide you, and it will do so. You would never make a mistake, no, never, if you were guided by your subconscious.

Say with all your heart, 'Let there be wealth' or 'Let there be health' or anything else you want, and these things are bound to manifest.

You must give a certain period each day to silence and meditation. Why must you do this? Because then you are converted into a transmitting station between your sub-conscious mind and yourself – your needs. Desire the conversation of none, just you and your subconscious talking things over together.

You may say that you have a lot to do in the home, your social life, the shop, in the factory, at the office, and you must press on as hard as you can to accomplish the task. But though it would seem the best possible thing to do, it is not. Call a halt now and again. Be still. Listen. Your load will be lightened. You will see how best to complete your work without effort. Many tycoons do this. They slip into their office quietly for a while, refusing to see anyone. They have a period of quiet meditation, and that's how they get on, and how they become millionaires. Do I do this at home or back-stage? Of course I do. There are times when I won't see any-one backstage, however eager the caller. I always take quiet-ness before a performance, more particularly, if I am going to read minds.

Stillness is an essential to any workable system of magic. Until this condition of self-disciplined solitude is achieved, it is useless to attempt any magical operation. You have been told how the Master Psychologist, who worked more dynamic magic than anyone has ever done, was reputed to have ascended a hill often, to be alone for long periods in order to become reinforced.

It is absolutely essential that you cultivate the art of stillness, physically and mentally. Like this, your subconscious can give you ideas so illuminating that success in whatever you are doing is a certainty. You need not be defeated by anything. You will get success techniques so that you become devastatingly sure of yourself.

Suddenly you are conscious that you are listening. It hardly seemed audible, yet you are sure you heard a whisper. But you are not quite certain. What you are certain of is an impelling urge, a sudden impulse to act, to do something, to go somewhere, to see someone. You feel guided. You know you must act on this guidance. You have a 'hunch', a premonition, and you must act on it. You are able to check unfavourable conditions, you are able to surmount difficulties, you are able to overcome hardships. You are directed. You are your own creator.

The first thing to do on entering your study, or when sitting alone on the hill, is to listen to your subconscious. Write the thoughts that come to you in a notebook which you are going to keep for that purpose, and be guided by them not leaving out a bit here and there, because it is not what you like. Carry out the guidance absolutely. You will get suggestions to come somewhere, do something. Go where you are told and do what you are impressed to do. Let your subconscious take full charge. You will then be guided to meet the people you should meet, to help you, or influenced to go to a certain place at a certain time. I knew someone who was 'told' to go to a certain place at a certain time, and he went. There he met a man he had not seen for many years; a man who was able to book him up for a long series of lectures. He was a lecturer and this meant big money for him. Listen, and you will be told what books to read, what magazine, what newspaper. And if you act on the guidance you will find something to help you in them.

If you go to a party or a meeting, on entering the room ask your subconscious who you should sit next to, and you will be 'told', and you will find that you are sitting next to

59

somebody who offers help, or to whom you can offer help. I have done this many times, and it always works out right.

In the silence of your room, your subconscious will take you 'above the pairs of opposites' (good and bad) and you will know and practise good only. You will gain the 'single eye' and become positive, blind to any form of negative thinking. With meditation you will be rightly directed. By contemplation you gradually become purified (like the Fire Walkers). You will feel ashamed to do or speak or think anything unworthy, you will shrink back from evil. You will feel inspired to high endeavours.

The more often you visit your 'retreat', the more you will like it. The less you go, the more you will loathe it. The more often you go to it the greater comfort it will become. Shut your eyes to outward things; prepare yourself more and more by daily practice, for the receiving of magical power. Ask your subconscious to grant you understanding. Reflect on your past negative outlook with great displeasure and grief. Examine your conscience and to the utmost of your power make it pure and clear.

Images are the language of the subconscious. If you hold the image of yourself as successful and prosperous as you meditate, it will deeply penetrate into your subconscious mind and if strong enough and deep enough, will act as an automatic brake against bad and negative impulses.

What has all this got to do with bringing out the magic in your mind? You are not concerned with character building, but working magic, getting the things you want.

Never forget the Fire Walkers; again I repeat, it is a matter of **purifying** yourself.

Listen to your subconscious during meditation. You may be told to pay that debt, instead of buying the new shoes you would like. Anyway, after you have paid that debt, you can still ask your subconscious to get you the shoes. You may have to listen to things about yourself you don't like very much. You must listen, accept, and go right through with it, or you must leave it alone. But you cannot work magic by doing only the things you like, and leaving out the rest.

You have the idea that, provided you know how to work magic, something may be got for nothing.

You can never bring something into possession that you have not earned, either by good character or actions.

I know a woman who wanted a king-sized caravan. She meditated upon this. She was impressed with the idea that she should start collecting things for it. She bought a miniature shovel for the fire, a guest towel, a duster. Every time she went into town she bought some little thing, because during meditation this idea came to her. The king-sized caravan came before long in quite a miraculous way. Her subconscious knew by her actions that she wanted it desperately and was prepared to buy little things to prove her eagerness.

The same with a man I know who got a nice car. He bought some wool and made himself a carpet for the car, because during meditation the idea was pressed home. He acted on it. The car came soon after, though at the time he could not see how he would ever get it.

Make your commands clear in every detail. Don't be like the woman who wanted a bowl of goldfish. She asked her subconscious for a bowl of fish, and she meditated upon it day after day.

Before very long a neighbour knocked on the door. 'I've brought you a bowl of fish,' she said. 'Fred caught more than we could possibly manage to eat,' and she handed over a plastic bowl with two trout in it!

So it had come true, in every detail. The bowl. The fish. Had she asked for a glass bowl with water in it, and goldfish swimming around in it, she would have got what she really wanted.

Meditate. Meditate properly. An old peasant was seated alone in the last pew of the village church. 'What are you waiting for?' I asked. 'I am looking at Him, and He is looking at me,' he said softly.

This is called 'silent contemplation'. And you can do this sort of contemplation with anything. Look at the thing you want, contemplate it quietly, by just looking. It will come, if all else is right with you.

You must meditate to get out of the jam you are in. The more you meditate the more you become to have a horror of wrong action, and take a greater and greater delight in generosity.

Most men and women today have grown up with harassed expressions, lined faces, bustling, fretting, complaining, bad-tempered, unhappy. This need not mean you. The secret lies in meditation. Here lies the strategy that frees you from the bad, the sad, the mad.

Perhaps you have grown irritated when the dinner is late. Angry when the soup is too thick. Perhaps you have cursed when the coffee is cold. Perhaps you have taken part in nagging because you are tired. Meditation will take away your tiredness. Meditation will lift you up.

Let the meditation of your heart and the power of your word be good. Is it good? Is it kind? The more pure you are the bigger magic you can do. You must try and refine yourself like gold in a furnace. You get nothing for nothing. You must earn it.

Is all this a disappointment? Is it too much trouble? Is it too big a price to pay? I don't think so. You want to work magic of a spectacular kind. And these are the 'musts'.

Spacemen searching distances almost too great for our imagination, find exquisite order, tidiness, and purpose in everything they see. Astronomers who discover a new planet millions of miles away, weighing millions of tons, and flying through space at thousands of miles an hour, find a wonderful order, never chaos. Everything follows clear-cut laws.

Day after day, night after night, century after century, this wonderful world goes on working in **perfect harmony**. Only man makes chaos and disharmony. Only man breaks **the laws**.

Meditate upon this. Determine there will be no more chaos in your life, no more muddling through. Lift your mind high, high above the stars, and meditate. Get the sort of silence where you will hear your wrist watch ticking for the first time in years.

This thought transmission between you and your subconscious during meditation is recognized by the Tibetans. At the close of day they invoke Peace to the vegetables, Peace to the animals, Peace to the elements, Peace to the living, Peace to the non-living, and Peace to all.

This thought transmission is stronger the purer you are, for then you can submit waves of higher frequency. Waves transmitted by silent meditation are more powerful and far-reaching, than the waves of the spoken word. Sometimes two people can meet, and convey a terrific lot, without saying a word. You can get a message over stronger and surer by silence than by words.

Meditate. You must go into the silence. To fly properly even aeroplanes spend most of their time on the ground! Stillness. Make a break with the negative past as clean as amputation.

'You mean it? I've got to be quiet, quiet, **quiet**?'

It's true, friend.

People who do brave things and great deeds, meditate. And they listen-in to their subconscious. Rear Admiral Richard Byrd, the great explorer and Commanding Officer of the United States Antarctic Service Expedition, broadcast on the eve of his departure for the Antarctic:

'It was on my lonely vigil during the long Polar night that I learnt the power of silence. The values and the problems of life sorted out when I began to listen. . . .'

See what I mean?

I am not an Antarctic explorer. I explore the mind. And if you want to know how I came to do that, I will tell you. I was a paratrooper in the war, and was shot down three times. I spent a year in hospital, for a long time unresponsive to treatment, but later the master of my own return to health by a sustained application of physiotherapy, psychiatry, and psychology. Stacks of books on psychology were given to me at the hospital. I used to sit up in bed and read them, one after the other, completely fascinated, determined to master it all. I was particularly interested in the subconscious mind, and studied everything I could get hold of on the subject. Let me quote what I said in the **Halifax Daily Courier and Guardian, September 6th, 1957**:

'**The voice of the subconscious is the greatest power in any one body and if only people knew how to use this power they could have anything they wanted from life, provided they knew first in their hearts that their particular ambition or wish was within the realms of possibility.**

There may be a price to pay, but there is no limit to the horizon if people would allow their subconscious to guide them. Brick walls there will always be, but there is always a way to the other side.'

You may think this is a bit fanciful, too good to be true, but **I crawled over that brick wall – and out of hospital**. It all comes under that one word, **Belief**.

I had plenty of time to meditate in that hospital bed for twelve months. Shell-shock is a terrible thing, and I asked myself, 'Why did this have to happen to me?' You get all your answers in the silence. I know that meditation is soothing, a comfort to one in distress, and it brings magic into your life. I know – because it's wonderfully true.

6
The Magic Of Love

LOVE has been recognized in the teaching engraved on the Sphinx: **Love is the Secret of Life;** in the caves of the Anchorites near Mount Sinai, **Love, with Wisdom, is the Secret of Life;** and again at the doorway of the great rock near Deir, Petraea, **The Torch of Life is fed by the oil of Love.**

Dr Voronoff tells us that it is love that causes the humble glow-worm to burn so brightly. And he reminds us of Victor Hugo's parting advice to his grandson Georges: **'Love, seek for love – love makes better men. You must love, my son, love well – all your life.'**

Love can bring out the magic in your mind, and it can bring out the magic in anyone with whom you come in contact. It was Barrie who said, 'That little bit more, how much it is.' Why cannot we love people more, show our love, help more, give more? Say to yourself again and again, 'I will try always to be in love.' In love with everything. When you love life you are able to say, 'This is my happy day.'

This so-called prosaic life is dull no longer when you are in love. You are a spirit on a sparkling star. The commonplace becomes beautiful, and the beautiful a thousand times more lovely.

'Oh, my dear, isn't it lovely!' The words may be applied to a single buttercup of the twenty million in one field, a golden sunbeam, a cathedral, a May morning, a blackbird's song, or a piece of bread and cheese. The music of a moth fluttering against a window, a waterfall, a violin. The world is full of lovely things. If you are content to live and die without having looked at the colour of the earth, or striven to give pleasure, you do not deserve to be alive in this magic, magnificent world.

A famous Stoic sage commanded: 'Love everything that happens to you.'

I love the things I am doing. I love going on the stage to perform magic or read somebody's mind. I love going before the television cameras. Yes, I mean it. And I love writing this book. (I hope you will love reading it!)

I love every minute of every day. Loving should be a real part of your life. You can adapt yourself to this new way of facing things, if you determine to do so. Love can lift you to the highest dimension, and that is where you must get.

I love my audiences everywhere, the car I drive, my home, my family, my tropical fish, my poodles.

I love the mountains, museums, music, and flowers.

The sky is never so blue, the birds never sing so sweetly, our friends are never so gracious, as when you are **filled with love**. Love raises you to heights otherwise quite impossible, where magic can be done almost instantly.

It is a psychological law that you cannot separate yourself from your own kind. The most sacred truth is violated when you consider yourself not one with your fellow men. History suggests the idea was born 5,000 years ago, but it is a fact, a fact which experience proves.

If you want magic to come, just throw away your old attitudes and beliefs. Throw them overboard at once. Love is an all-important law of magic. See no difference between ant and angel, between white and coloured people. Look at the ocean and not the wave. We are all a part of the same. Every worm is a brother of the Nazarene.

This spirit of all-embracing love is the outcome of the understanding that all living things, from man down to the earth-worm, are subject to the same laws and conditions of existence.

'As I am, so are they; as they are, so am I.' One should identify oneself with all that lives, and should not kill or hurt any living being.

The Buddhists call this love **Metta**. It is that innermost wish that all living beings without exception, may be happy, free from pain and grief.

We should overflow with love, embracing the low and the high, the ugly and the beautiful, the sinful and the virtuous alike. This is possible only to one who adopts the right attitude. And unless you perfect yourself and attain this right attitude, all attempts at magic are fruitless. Because all this sort of thing comes under the heading of **purification**. To work magic, and keep on working magic, you must have a loving heart. The more you can develop this disposition in yourself, the more you will realize your ambitions. You will have wonderful power. Magic and miracles are not a part of your life at the moment, but soon – if you really follow all that I am saying – you will be able to achieve your wildest dreams. The light which shines in your aura is conditioned by the qualities of your character. The better and purer you are, the greater the light, and depending on its brilliance is whether or not you can really work wonders. The only passport required for entrance into the world of magic is an earnest desire to know. And I am giving you that knowledge.

It means persistence on your part. All the qualifications to work magic are not easy of attainment, but this much is certain, they **can** be attained, if you are determined not to be beaten. The way will unfold step by step as you read this book. March on boldly. Be patient. Be courageous. Be regular in your meditation. Be calm and love, no matter what befalls you. The end of wisdom is freedom; all will be yours when you are wise to all this. The end of knowledge is love. Love is a conquering force. Love is the magic key that opens any door. Cultivate love every day, and every moment.

You must awaken this dormant power, the primary principle, which is in your mind and back of magic phenomena. Your very life can be a practical demonstration of the reality of magic.

One, perchance, in thousands of men, strives for perfection. One, perchance, among those striving, knows how to perform magic. The doubting self goes to destruction. There must be self-control and self-discipline.

Do you love the work you are doing? Here is a story that illustrates what I mean:

' 'ow long 'ave yer bin at this job that yer in such a 'urry?' said one of the characters to an old roadmender in a book by Michael Fairless.

'Four months,' he replied.

'Seen better days?'

'Never,' he said emphatically.

'Mean ter say yer like crackin' these blamed stones to fill 'oles some other fool's made?'

He nodded assent.

'Well, that beats everything. Now, I've seen better days; worked in a big brewery over near Maidstone – a town that, and something doing; and now, 'ere I am, 'ammering me 'eart out on these blasted stones for a bit of bread and a pipe of baccy once a week – it ain't good enough.'

Here you have two men doing the same job. But they are different men. One is happy and loves his work, the other complains and is discontented. They have different attitudes. And you know which of those two could work magic, if he wanted to.

Do you love your neighbour, however poor? Here is another story. It is of two very poor women who lived in a slum alley. One had love in her heart, but the other was a negative type.

68

The two back doors of these people used to face each other, and the negative woman when she was swilling out the yard one day got a brush and brushed the water for all she was worth in big splashes into the other woman's doorway. Her steps were wet and it went into the room. She did not like the woman or was jealous of her for some reason, and she showed her spite in this unkindly manner.

What did the neighbour do? Did she rave at the woman for her beastly low-down trick, did she bellow back at her horrid names?

No. She was a positive woman and had love in her heart. She lived life happily, and there she sat in her little room letting the woman do as she pleased. And all the while she held the thought: Bless you. Bless you.

There came a big breeze later and the woman's washing was hanging and blowing about on the line. The clothes-prop was none too safe in the fierce gusts, and suddenly a mighty wind blew the thing down.

The little woman who had been treated so unkindly could see what was about to happen, and she ran out of the room where she was sitting and just caught the prop in time to save her neighbour's clean washing from falling into the wet yard which she had just been swilling.

When the negative unkind woman saw how good her neighbour had been after the horrid thing which she had done to her she was amazed. She could not believe her eyes. But that little love action changed her from a bad woman into a good one. The two women became wonderful friends.

You see, the woman with love in her heart was too big to be hurt.

If a man hits you on the cheek, offer him the other also. If a man hits you and you hit back, it shows that you know no more about love than the other man.

If a person steals your coat, give him the other coat also. Say: 'You have wanted this of me, take it and let me help you still more. Let me comfort you.' That thing has happened as a test, to see how much love you have in your heart for humanity. The way that you will meet that experience will prove absolutely whether you understand the meaning of love or not. If you have placed yourself under the law of love you know that all is well. You have acquired the good disposition. You know that that man is only your brother, and it is really your brother you are giving the thought to.

If you retaliate, if you do what he did, it shows that you do not know anything more about working magic than he does.

Say 'Perhaps you need my other coat? What prompted you to steal?' You may be astounded at the story you may get from that man.

Take your love tests victoriously. It is the mind that will work magic.

Let people try hard to hurt you. Let them try hard to get you into a temper. Let them try hard to make you pass an adverse criticism about some aspect of life. **But let it be of no use.**

Never complain. Get rid of your lower self and put your greater self in its place. Accept life. Love everything that happens to you, because it gives you a chance to prove yourself. It gives you a chance to bring out the magic in your mind.

Let me tell you the charming story of a girl of thirteen, who had to bring up a family and run a home. Then she fell ill. Worn out, she lay in hospital, and a church worker visited her in the ward. One of the first questions he asked the little girl as she lay dying was: 'Have you been confirmed?'

The little girl said, 'No.'

Then the church worker asked: 'What are you going to say to God when you have to tell Him that?'

The child's eyes held a peace too deep to be disturbed, and she said simply, 'I . . . I . . . shall show Him my hands.'

Her hands, poor child, were her proof of love. She had lived a life of unselfishness and love. She had given all that

70

was good in herself, regardless of her health, to others. This love is without selection or exclusion.

If you love a few friends and exclude unpleasant people, or those whom you look upon as enemies, then you do not get the idea of what I mean by love. Love is not only brotherly feeling, but a principle. It is principle I am driving into you all the time. You must **live to principle**, if you would attempt feats of magic. The love I mean is the dynamic suffusing of every living being, excluding none whatsoever. If your intentions are intense enough, loving actions will follow automatically.

Pure love must embrace all beings everywhere, and all creatures. And we are striving for purity (remember the Fire Walkers). Love is one of the most significant things in life, yet somehow most of us are afraid to show it. You may say you want to make a demonstration of affection, **but you never get round to it!** You want to, but you can't.

Let yourself go. These three words should be underlined in your mind. Let yourself go, if you want to work magic and if you want to bring out the magic in somebody else. If you fail to express love then you restrain your actions and become negative at once, completely without magnetism.

You must have active love in your life. Age doesn't matter. When you are a hundred you still have the same feelings inside of you; still desire to love and be loved. You will get a glowing reaction from your friends, your relations, the old and lonely, and the very young.

Love can be defined in one word – **giving.** Give of yourself with sincerity and deep feeling.

Think of Christmas. What a time it is for giving. Love shines in the paper decorations hanging from the ceiling. Love shines in the coloured electric lights festooned around the Christmas tree.

Two thousand years ago in a lowly stable in Bethlehem, a Divine Child was born, turning the world into a fairyland for one day. It is better than millions of diamonds to be loved by

71

children, to see the stars in their eyes, hear the music of their laughter.

Christmas is a magic time. It is made magic through a world in love. For a little while it changes everybody. People laugh and love again in the infectious gaiety of the greatest Festival of all time. That is love. The love that transfigured a family at Bethlehem.

You should meditate on love. According to the Buddhist method, training oneself comes first. They strive for individual perfection before all else. From trained minds come right thoughts, right actions, and right words. The Buddhists call this Metta (Loving-kindness). They say mentally, 'May I be well and happy,' and after a while they extend it to all others, saying, 'May all beings of the Universe be well and happy.' They mean it, and they feel it. They send out these thoughts of Metta before they go to sleep. They maintain these thoughts of Metta (Loving-kindness) and they have serene, peaceful, and successful lives. There is great poise and serenity in their faces, in their whole personality.

The Buddhist works on himself first. When they meditate on love, they meditate on love of self first. (May I be free from harm.) Pure love comes first. By having pure love (Metta) as they define it, for self, selfish tendencies, hatred, anger, become diminished. They believe that unless they themselves possess Metta within, they cannot share; they cannot radiate, they cannot send this Metta to others. According to Buddhism, as I said before, self-love comes first. If a person cannot help himself well, they say, they cannot help others well. Metta is much more than ordinary affection; it means a great deal more than loving-kindness, really. Metta is much higher; to obtain Metta you reach the very highest plane. And isn't that what we must do? In meditation they do not merely think about it, they 'become' it. Loving-kindness can be maintained towards a person with whom you are annoyed, this is how annoyance with him can be removed.

72

A Buddhist's thoughts in meditation go something like this: 'May all breathing things . . . all beings . . . all persons . . . be freed from distress and anxiety, and may they guide themselves to bliss. May all creatures in the **eastern direction** be freed from distress, and may they guide themselves to bliss. May all creatures in the **western direction** . . . in the **northern direction** . . . in the **southern direction** . . . be freed from distress, and guide themselves to bliss.'

People have said to me, 'Should we love snakes – should we love mice?'

In the world of magic, we aim at the highest form of love, and I say 'yes'. Love is the best state of heart in the world, and a state that will bring the magic out of your mind, and out of the minds of those with whom you come in contact.

All people and all nations should live on the principle of no hate, no fear, no greed. The prelude to this is that everybody and every nation begins that new quality of living now. Then we shall be able to say, 'Behold how these nations love one another.'

Watch the effect of love upon a person. Sound the trumpets, beat the drums, and see his countenance brighten and the glowing light of satisfaction come into his eyes.

Dogs, horses, cats, even birds, respond to love and rebel at blame or censure. Any gardener knows that flowers you love to tend, even bless, will bloom better and last far longer than those you are not interested in. And he knows that flowers tended without thought and feeling, even sometimes cursed, will quickly hang their heads and die.

It is the same with objects. A man can walk into an engine-room and trouble starts at once. Things go wrong. It would seem that even **things** have likes and dislikes. An engineer who loves his machine can talk to his engine, polish it, call it 'old girl'; generally sympathize with it, in fact. And it is receptive at once. It works for such a personality. The magic of love does the trick. It has been scientifically proved that metal atoms can become tired; gold, silver, zinc, copper, iron – these responsive atoms will co-operate or not, according to the type of personality dealing with them.

Where there is love there is communication. It is as though things **know** your thoughts and how you feel towards them. The same thing happens with water and chemicals; they have their likes and dislikes, their attractions and repulsions. But love is the magic that can put things right, the magic that will get you what you want. Have you never tried it on your car; it goes wrong, you swear, you cannot get it to go. Somebody comes along to give you a hand, probably somebody who hasn't got a car, and would like one (one like yours, perhaps). They have only to look at it, and the trouble becomes righted. Love. What a magical word it is.

How do you feel when you want to love everybody and everything? You feel joyful, free, open-minded, happy. With love, life is very sweet on this earth with its daffodils in the springtime.

Hans Andersen understood love. To put it in a nutshell, here is his story:

There was an old man who had a horse. He thought it would be best if he sold the horse or exchanged it for something more useful. But what?

His wife said: 'You will know best, old man.'

So he exchanged it for a cow.

Then he exchanged the cow for a sheep.

Coming across a man with a goose under his arm, he exchanged the sheep for a goose.

Soon afterwards he exchanged the goose for a fowl, but when he came across an ostler with a sack of rotten apples, he exchanged the fowl for the rotten apples.

The old man related the story of his exchange to someone, who said assuredly: 'Well, your old woman will give it to you when you get home!'

But he answered, 'She will kiss me and say, "What the old man does is always right." '

When he got home he told his wife how he exchanged the horse for a cow.

'Heaven be thanked,' she said.

. . . how he exchanged the cow for a sheep.

'Ah, better still,' she said.

'. . . but I exchanged the sheep for a goose.'

'You are always thinking of something to give me pleasure,' she continued.

And when he told her how he gave away the goose for a fowl, she complimented him on the good exchange.

'But I exchanged the fowl for a sack of shrivelled apples.'

(Think of it.) What would the ordinary woman say? How would she feel about it? I am afraid she would be in a violent temper. Certainly she would not love him for it.

But Hans Andersen makes his character exclaim most excitedly, 'I must positively **kiss** you for **that**, my dear good husband!'

Here is the true story of a man who knew the meaning of love. When a car plunged into the water at Cardiff Docks, this young man made a perfect dive, brought the driver ashore, then hurried away before anybody could speak to him.

'A marvellous dive!' said onlookers. But they never knew how wonderful till it was discovered that the young man, William Hunter, of Cardiff, had lost an arm and a leg in an accident when he was thirteen.

It seems impossible that he could have done such a thing, but where there is love, there is magic.

George Sanders, the famous film star, had been very ill, and nobody seemed to be getting him right. Then he met a man who summed up his trouble at once. He was an intelligent man. The secret of renewed health was uttered by him in one word – **Love**.

'Love everyone,' he said. 'It is the only solution.' George Sanders looked amazed, he was flabbergasted. 'I know it's hard,' said the man, 'but you must make the effort.'

And he did.

And it is the teaching of the Buddha. Without fire and sword, Buddhism has found its way into the hearts of millions and millions of beings. From history we know that, since the time of the Buddha up to this day, **not a single drop of blood** has been shed in the name of the Buddha. This is a big thing to say, but it is true, and that is how love works. I am not trying to make everybody a Buddhist, I am merely giving you the facts of love, in these people, because love is what we are talking about; love is what we must have in our lives if we are going to bring out the magic in our minds. To work magic you have got to be a little more kind, a little more sympathetic, you have got to have a little more belief in the other fellow, a little more patience, and a little more of what the Great Psychologist called **Love**.

Somebody said to me the other day, 'I've got to leave Hereford, after living there all these years. I've got a job in Birmingham, and I've got to go and live there. Do you think I shall like Birmingham – I mean the people?'

'What did you think of Hereford? What did you think of the people?'

'Oh, Hereford's a lovely city, but rotten people. I don't like them at all.'

I said, 'Then you won't like Birmingham. You won't like the people there.'

He looked disappointed, but don't you see, it was his **attitude**. Such a man would not like people anywhere he went. He did not know the meaning of love.

The very stones of Paris speak of love. In Paris there is no pretence that love is unimportant or unworthy. They know it for what it is, the one big thing that lifts man above the brute and shows him the reflection of the stars even in the gutter. Love gives you a momentary glimpse of something rarer, finer, more poetic.

If you don't love now; a human, your environment, your life, you might well begin to learn. Not the love that any fool can feel when he stops his car in a bluebell wood on a Sunday morning in May but that which sustains you when the sun isn't shining, and the bluebells are dead, and you can't afford a car any longer and are too ill to drive it if you could.

Not a place in your heart anywhere for love? I think love is the only true value, whether it's for someone or for something. You may work hard and do everything else that is necessary to perform magic, but without love you cannot reach the fourth-dimension; you cannot become magnetic; you cannot achieve success, or attract that Jaguar, that motor yacht, that beautiful house you have always wanted. Perhaps it doesn't make sense to you, that one has to do so many things and believe so many things, in order to bring out the magic in your mind, but it is true. Better get out your exercise book and write in it a hundred times, 'I must not be small-minded.'

The world needs magic. The world needs love. You can be the best of all magicians, if you follow what I say. Don't turn your back on anything. Make up your mind that you are going to get everything in the world you want – easily – quickly – by magic.

I am continually getting the things I want and I can say that life is wonderful. When I started this book, when I got the idea of writing it, I just could not see how in the world I would ever have time to do it. But the way opened, and a way will always open if you want a thing intensely enough, and are prepared to make sacrifices.

I said a little while ago that you have to become as a little child. The poet, Francis Thompson, says:

'Know you what it is to be a child . . . it is to believe in love . . . to believe in loveliness . . . to believe in belief. . . .'

One of the finest examples of love is the moving and heroic story of Dr David Spencer, who gave a comparative stranger one of his kidneys to try and save his life.

It was Dr Ian Clark. He took over his patients, and the glowing accounts they gave of Clark made him begin to envy him. Everyone sang his praises, and he began to hate him, hate him, hate him.

But when he met Dr Ian Clark, he lost some of the jealousy. His ideas changed. He realized all that the patients had been saying was true. And he agreed with them.

Dr David Spencer and Dr Ian Clark talked together for hours, and he began to look up to him and admire him tremendously.

It does not alter the fact that this heroic man made the sick doctor a gift of one of his kidneys at the time when he hated him. He did it to save the life of a stranger! Have you ever heard of such an astonishing thing? Wonderful, isn't it? Hope died and flickered away, but this man's great demonstration of love will never die. Would you risk your life to rave a colleague? To save a stranger? To save someone you disliked? I think it is a splendid example of love.

Love can be a poem, like the noblest monument ever raised by a man to his beloved, the beautiful Taj Mahal of Agra. The Emperor Shah of Jehan built for his adored Mumtaz this monument of loving devotion, so beautiful that rough-hewn men have cried when they first beheld its loveliness. This flame that is called love can lead us to the stars, or it can lead us to the scaffold. It depends on ourselves. Some of us do not think about it at all, yet a touch of romance could make the situation magic.

It is not easy to love. We must ask our subconscious for guidance. We may be called upon to apply the law of forgiveness and wipe out the past, never an easy thing to do. We may be told to forgive all who have wronged us, through thought, word, and deed. Nurse Cavell put it this way, 'I must have no hatred or bitterness toward anyone.'

Is there somebody who dislikes you? Somebody you meet every day? Somebody whose guts you hate?

Well, if he behaves like a boor it's almost certain he's afraid. He has a negative attitude to life. He may have had a lot of worries and disappointments that have made him a little sour.

But there is some good in him somewhere. Try to find it. Don't let his behaviour bother you. Be extra kind.

A Stockholm doctor once tried out a very interesting experiment. He took photos of human faces and found that if he superimposed fourteen or more photos on top of each other the resulting common face was **always** beautiful. He tried again and again, but it always worked out the same – something **beautiful** was there. And that is how you should look at people – all the people you meet or see during the day – mix them up and know that there is something good there somewhere.

Do you greet the daybreak buoyantly, filled with the thought of what this day may enable you to do for another's sake? To lessen pain, to impart happiness, to help with all the means that you have at your disposal, filled with love and self-forgetfulness?

Suppose, then, you start your day by saying, 'I send a blessing to everyone I meet today, to each one I speak to, to each one on whom my glance rests.' What a wonderful beginning. To start your day like that is to understand the fourth-dimension of kindness all right.

Stage people are well known for their spirit of comradeship. Whatever show you belong to, you work together as a team. You are like a big happy family. You leave one theatre and go to another, and everyone treats you with this same brotherly or sisterly feeling. Instantly you are welcomed, usually called by your first name, with a 'dear' attached for warmth and chumminess. It doesn't happen outside the theatre, only when there is a war on, or a long spell of deep snow. Then everyone becomes friendly, everybody is out to help each other. But one does not see this sort of behaviour in ordinary times.

On some occasions I ask the audience to participate. Would, say, two ladies and two gentlemen come up on the stage to take part in this next act of magic?

A shy young lady steps up, or is it nervousness? I put her at ease, or try to.

'What's your name, dear?'

She speaks very quietly, 'Gypsy.'

'A little louder, dear, please.'

'Gypsy.'

'Is it really?'

She nods.

'That's very pretty. Now, would you mind picking out an envelope, dear?'

She does so.

'I hope you will be very lucky.'

And so on. By now she has lost her shyness. She has melted to the warmth of that one little word dear.

'Dear' is an expression of love for humanity, a psychological touch that works magic. You get co-operation at once, and she gets a cheer from the audience.

The other day a woman said of a man, 'If he calls me dear, I'll smack his face!'

Never, never in a thousand years could such a person work magic.

7
The Secret Of Wealth

SOME people have the secret of wealth. They have got marvellous principles, and they know how to work magic that brings them plenty of money. Some people will do anything for you, they will forget and they will forgive. They will take the shirt off their backs to help you. It is their disposition. That is why they are prosperous.

They have been brought up to love money, and to understand it. When they were children their parents let them play with money on the table, and play with money on the floor. They let them play with money, rather than other things children play with, like teddy bears and engines. And when they send them to a shop, these children know the value of money, and you can't fool them. They have grown up sane about handling cash and notes, and they know how to live prosperously.

Have you taught your children the value of money? No. Most children are never taught. Mothers have said, 'Never do anything for money, dear.' Think how they have closed their channels. You have to learn to open those channels again and understand the law that 'it is only as we **give**, that we receive'.

Watch the children of money-conscious parents. They will play at store with other children. They will have pins, matches, sugar, tea, soap, all sorts of things in their toy store to exchange. Business methods should be taught from boyhood. They are taught how to trade from little babies. It is not long before they have everything from the others, they give, and give, and give of their supplies, and they have to run home to mother for more. The shrewdness of these children and the ignorance of the untaught children is astounding. It is no wonder they grow up to be successful, they understand the law of exchange. They know that it is absolutely as you give that you receive.

You have got to make yourself a channel, a magnet, and keep your channel open and your mind alert. If you do not speak to your subconscious every day and command money (and know in your heart because you have asked, it is coming), then you are not alert. You have to ask incessantly, and make yourself so glad that it is coming, that you can hardly contain your joy. Make yourself as excited and happy as though someone had told you that you have a million pounds coming to you. Why, you would not be able to sleep at night. Make yourself that glad. Believe it.

The money-conscious parent teaches the child wealth wants me, not I want wealth. And they are taught to love it and welcome it. This is the difference between you and the other fellow.

Ask, and you will get it. Never stop asking till you do get it. If you do not get it straight away, it is your test. Pass it victoriously. Continue to believe, for when you have once passed your test you do not have a similar test again. Keep on and on. Do not take 'no' for an answer.

Some people say 'when my ship comes in'. Good gracious, it has been in the harbour for years waiting to be unloaded, and you didn't know it!

Know that you can begin unloading your ship today. It is in the harbour, and your belief will materialize it. Your belief will help you to unload it. There is no lack in the world, the lack is in you, and if you will stop seeing lack and stop thinking lack, and see abundance and think abundance, you will make marvellous demonstrations.

Get money if only for the satisfaction it will give you when you have got it. You can always give it away if you don't really want it. But **do be rich**. When you sing, 'Mercy drops round me are falling,' you are mad. Yes, you are. You are negative and not in your right mind. You do not want 'mercy drops', you want 'showers in plenty'. And you can get it if you are positive. Get a new understanding of money.

Do you bless every penny that you send out, and command it to return to your multiplied a millionfold, that you may have plenty in your storehouse? Many wealthy people do this, and do it regularly. They do not bless their money in a haphazard way. They do it with faith and with reverence. They treat it sacredly.

If you are in earnest and you have belief, and you bless your money, asking it to return to you multiplied, **it will do so**. If you command big money, with belief in your heart, you will receive big money. But there must always be action.

Work hard at your business or profession, fill in the pools if you want to, but **do something**.

Money! Stacks of it! Wads of crisp notes and bags of shining silver. What dreams it conjures up for us, doesn't it? If only you could win the pools, or get a mighty windfall, the world would be your oyster, wouldn't it? You could do anything, have anything, go anywhere. You wouldn't feel tired any more; you would feel young and boisterous. Your belief can win you a prize so big in money that you will be staggered. Your belief can bring you a windfall so enormous that you could only think you were dreaming. Solomon said there was a **'Time for everything,'** and at the right time you will get it, if you believe. There are unseen powers at work for you. And the unseen is what does the trick; ask any magician.

What shall it be? A voyage around the world? A castle?

Racehorses, your own 'plane, or just a swimming pool in the garden? You have only to make up your mind and work with the law.

Another secret of some people's great prosperity is that they carry in their pocket or handbag a **roll of notes** that they can hardly span – rolled tight. They do not carry small coins, because like attracts like, so they would only get small coins.

When you send your money out, remember always to **bless** it. Ask it to bless everybody that touches it, and command it to go out and feed the hungry and clothe the naked, and command it to come back to you a millionfold. Don't pass over this lightly. I am serious. Bless it (Abracadabra – speak the blessing) is what every magician does before he works magic. I have said this before, but it is important that you remember it.

There is a vast difference between sending out your money without any thought, or sending it out with a thought that it is going to multiply. It is wonderful, really, because it does work magic. It does bring results.

You must never be without money in your wallet or your purse. Money is a magnet. Without money in your wallet how can you attract money? Money draws money. Like attracts like. Carry a five-pound note 'for luck', and you will attract five-pound notes! Do not carry a penny or a three-penny bit. It will bring you its own like. A penny or three-pence is all that will come to you. The thing you want, that you've got to be. If you want to be wealthy, you have got to represent wealth. So make sacrifices and save; save until you can carry a five-pound note around with you.

Visualize intensely. If you have a one-pound note in your hand **see** three noughts after it – that makes it one thousand. You send that vision out and it **has** to manifest itself to you. It is the law of visualization. You have got to **expand in consciousness.** You must not be content to deal in threepences. A Bank Manager once told me, 'You'd be surprised the number of people who collect threepenny bits.' Well, that is all they will ever draw to them. That is not the way to work magic.

I refuse to look at a penny or a threepenny bit more than I can possibly help. If I have a penny I usually leave it in my pocket, and change a sixpence or a shilling. You must see silver and not coppers. Get rid of coppers as soon as you can. I do. I won't have anything to do with them if I can help it. You cannot draw shillings to you if you see pennies. It is what you see that matters. You must spend silver, you must spend notes, you must see them all the time. Get rid of your coppers, or change them quickly into silver. **Refuse to deal in little coins.** You have got to enlarge your consciousness, you have got to get the rich consciousness.

Never give a penny in a collection. If you do, that is all you will get back. **As you give you receive.** I must keep drumming this into you. I want you never to forget it. 'That thou see-est, that thou be-est.' Train yourself to deal in silver or notes, and before long you will be much better off. You have got to see the larger denomination. Some people can never think beyond silver, and they think they are doing fine. I am telling you what I know from experience draws money to you. And quickly.

The Master Psychologist gave the world the finest **get-rich-quick** method ever known. The first law of business is **give and take.** But always it is to be **give** first and **take** second. You have got to give before you can take.

I know a woman who put a pound note in a collection and she said she would never forget it. She felt so **rich.** She gave it, not of her abundance, but of her necessity. But she felt as though she owned the universe. 'It was a wonderful feeling,' she said.

She blessed the money and wished it was much more that she was giving, and three days later, from a quite unexpected source, she received very much more money back than she had given!

This is the great secret of money magic. You must bless

85

your money when you send it out, and you must ask it to return multiplied. It will. I assure you it will.

Did you ever see a prosperous man counting his money with a long face, damp his fingers, and turn the notes away from him as he counts those he is getting out of the pack for you? Never. He knows better. He smiles, damps his fingers, and turns the notes towards him, and he is thinking with that smile, 'They're coming back . . . they're coming back. . . .'

And roll your notes (if you haven't got any now, you should have plenty by the time you have finished reading this book). Put an elastic band around them, because, don't you see, it represents without beginning and without end. So that you may never begin to want, and your money will never end. Lots of monied people do that.

Bless your money every morning. Start your day right. Get into the habit of thinking in thousands. See thousands of notes. And when you project your thoughts into this electromagnetism, it has to take place.

When money begins to come in you must use it for whatever you have asked it for. A mother asks for money for a new dress, but when the money comes she buys trousers for Tommy. She has misappropriated that money, and violated the law.

Another thing you can do is fold a note in half, long ways, then fold it into three, to make a triangle when the two ends meet. This represents the Trinity, and represents a blessing of money for you.

I have actually known people to kiss their money good-bye. Never say good-bye, never think good-bye, either to friends or money. Words are creative. Choose the right words. I remember having done it before I came into the knowledge. If you say good-bye you separate yourself from your money substance. When you give it out and you never expect it to return to you again, then you deliberately sever your connection between you and your money. That money does not want to come back to you, and it will not do so, either.

86

Love money. People say sometimes that it is wicked to love money, but it is not. If you had five thousand pounds given to you today, you could do wonderful things, not only for yourself but for others. Yet you could draw many thousands more if you would only work the law.

The best way to get money that is owing to you is to **give** it to that person who owes it. Do not put anyone in bondage. When you loan a person money and exact an interest, and they have nothing at all, you are putting that person in bondage to you. You are tying their hands and closing their channels. What you do to the other fellow you get back. You put yourself under the law when you bondage another, 'Thou shalt not,' and if you do, you have to pay, an eye for an eye, and a tooth for a tooth. And you will find yourself indebted to someone else. Never bondage anyone. Never loan. Give it, that is the way to get money.

You have got to get the rich consciousness. I have said that before, but it is important. It is not the rich consciousness you possess when you bondage another. You must give it.

That 'plenty of wealth' has got to be in your mind and in your heart. If you do not feel rich in your mind, how are you going to feel rich in your wallet? What about your idea? If your idea is rich, will not your thoughts be rich? Declare day after day, 'I am rich. I am rich. I have sown my seed.' Do you think it is going to take the form of an empty wallet if you take your creation that far? Never. By thinking the rich word, the right thought, you produce plenty. Everything has to start in the mind. There is simply nothing in this world that does not come out of mind.

If you cannot get your bills paid, don't get into a temper as so many people do. Sit in the silence and tell those people they are honest and upright, and that you know they are coming to you to pay their bills. Send love. Bless them. Say, 'I have faith in you.'

There was a man who stole money from his employer and nobody could find where he had gone. But the employer was an unusual man and what he did was devote a certain time each day to sit in the silence. He would send that man love. 'I have faith in you,' he would think. 'I know you are coming back to make good.'

Time went on, but the day came when the thief returned. He was in tatters and rags, and his feet were bleeding. He knelt before his employer. 'Here I am,' he said. 'I give myself up to you – do with me as you want to.'

Imagine the situation. What did the employer do? Did he turn round and swear at him – have him up for robbery? Indeed no. 'God bless you,' he said, 'I knew you would come back and make good.'

' "... come back and make good." Why, that is all I have heard, day after day,' the thief said. 'Aren't you going to have me arrested?'

'No,' said the employer. 'You are going to make good and I am going to give you a job.' And that man took him back, because it was up to him to do it, and the thief turned out a splendid man.

There are some people who forgive what they cannot get in seven years. They write out a receipt in full for what is owing so that the unfortunate one can start afresh. You do the same thing – in mind – and it works in the same way. You go into the silence and give all the money that is owing you – then watch it come right up to your place of business – every penny of it. Wealth wants you, and if your heart is in the right place, it will come to you, heaped up, pressed down, and running over.

Give a tenth of your money to the sick and the poor and the needy, if you do not do this, you stop your flow of money.

Ten per cent of your money must be put aside for those in distress.

Your tithe money is for the poor who come to you for help. Your tithe belongs first to the poor, and because people have failed to do that, they become poor themselves. Your subconscious will draw to you the ones you have to look after out of that tithe money, so you need never, as long as you live, refuse to help anyone.

You cannot loan that money. You must give that money. Think how wonderful it is to one who is passing through the dark night of the soul, to have someone come and say, 'Here, brother, don't worry, you won't be thrown out of your house.' You pay the rent the first week, and the second and the third, if needs be. Your subconscious has led you to that family who are so poor, to help them until they are able to get on their feet, and what a blessing it is. How many are in this position today because somebody has failed to do their duty? In being kind you give these people faith again, and show them how to be a good steward to others. That is why some people are so rich and able to give thousands to charity. It is because money is coming in so fast they do not know what to do with it. **And it is coming in from this tithe.** I have never known anyone to tithe properly, and not receive a thousand times more than they have given. It may not come back all at once, but it certainly does come. As I said before, 'heaped up, pressed down, and running over'!

The first time I tithed I received not only a bigger return in actual cash than I had given, but more stage work came to me from the most unexpected sources. And what a supreme sense of uplift you feel when you tithe for the first time. You know in that glorious moment that it is divinely right and that you must follow it. You feel that at long last you are taking the right step.

Tithing fulfils the law of increase. Your supply of money will be greatly increased.

Charles Fillmore started forty years ago with seven pennies in this world, but he blessed those seven pennies and he began to tithe even on that small amount. Every day he would go into the silence and bless humanity; it only takes a moment or two. Now he has property valued more than eighteen millions. He gets money from all over the world.

89

That is exactly what you can do. Every day you can bless somebody else.

There is no race of people so forgiving as the Jewish race. There is no race of people who can stand the insults and abuse as the Jews, and can serve you with a smile on their face and call you 'my dear' – a typical expression. No race of people can take insults so kindly.

When you give, you must deem it a pleasure to give. Have two wallets, one for your tithe money, and one for your own personal money.

If you have no financial reserves whatever, be prepared to deny yourself something until you get it. Hold on to half of it. A millionaire told me how, before he became wealthy, he always 'saved half and spent half', however small the amount. He made it a principle. Immediately you have scraped together a nice little bit, you must plan to make more money from it. You must let this idea sink deep into your subconscious. Saving up alone is not enough. You will not find it easy to hold on to your cash. Everybody will be after it. But don't loan – **give**, as I said before. Give out of your tithe, not out of the money you are saving and going to make work for you. Get money, keep money to work for you, make it grow. You must act. You must find ways and means of making money work for you.

'Money is the root of all evil,' it is said. 'Money isn't everything.' These silly expressions are uttered by the unintelligent. Many people talk about money foolishly.

And you must be 'seen'. Take yourself where riches are. Take yourself to the very best hotel for tea or go to a famous and smart hotel bar for a drink. Holiday at the places where wealthy people congregate. If you can't afford it right now, make sacrifices until you have put away enough to do it. Go to Monte Carlo, St Moritz, anywhere on the Riviera where rich people can be seen, and where they can see you.

Go to the Premiere of a Film or the Royal Command Performance, anywhere where you can rub shoulders with wealthy people. And if you know of anyone who really knows how to make money, by hook or by crook, determine to meet them. Very often this is done through some hobby, which gives an excuse to get in touch. Try to get personally acquainted with those who know how to make money, those who have nice homes and big cars. Like attracts like. And if it is riches you are after, get in that environment as much as you can. Live in 'the rich end' of the town.

As soon as you make up your mind that one day soon you will have a lot of money, you lay the groundwork for a series of causes which will unleash forces to bring big results.

Spending money to give other people a treat is said to be very lucky. Good luck comes to anyone who gives pleasure to others. Money is 'made round to go round' and one who spends freely seems always to have money, whereas the one who is over-careful never seems to have any. Windfalls and money prizes come to those who are generous. 'To him that hath, shall be given.' Behave as you would if you had plenty. You are not generous if you give only to your own family. That is your duty. You are not generous if you give only that which you think you can afford. It is when you make sacrifices and do without something in order to make somebody else happy, that you become a generous person.

When you were very young you expected money off your parents, off aunts and uncles who called at the house, or a visitor who just popped in for a while. You expected sixpence or a shilling or half a crown. That **expectancy** got it for you. The magic of getting is **expectancy**.

You give of your tithe to those in trouble, you give to your own flesh and blood, you give to this and you give to that. But do you spend money to give others a nice surprise? These actions set up good magnetic vibrations.

Does happiness mean having plenty of money? Would you like to be 'rolling in money', or just have enough to get by?

I know all the answers. You want more money. Why not? You have never had it so good, perhaps, but you want it a lot better. You want success symbols to show the world how well you are progressing. A television set larger than your next-door neighbour's, a swing hammock for the garden, a washing machine and spin drier, a flashy car, holidays abroad, a week-end cottage with roses round the door. You want things to show for all the hard work you are doing.

Money! Money! Money!

Remember Roy Rogers, the multi-millionaire film star, King of the Cowboys? How did he get so rich?

Roy would not tolerate lying, or not keeping a promise. Grace before meals was part of routine in the ranch where he and his family lived: 'Lord, I thank you for this food, my work, and my wonderful friends. Thank you for everything, and make us better people.' Yes, that was what he used to say.

And that 'everything' included three luxurious cars, eight Palomino horses, 350 acres of grain at Lake Hughes, 1,200 acres of grazing at Marysville, 200 head of prize Herefords, quite apart from the immense income from show business; stage, television, films, records, and broadcasting.

Every week he would make long-distance telephone calls to thirty or forty children who were all ill, injured or in trouble, and he would give them a simple 'pep' talk, like the psychologist that he was. He adored helping youngsters. When asked the secret of his fantastic fortune, he said: 'The big reason for my success is that the kids remember me in their prayers.'

He was a wonderful man and he observed the laws of getting. He tried to be **pure**; no lies, no broken promises. He observed the laws of giving, and gave to everyone, particularly children. He was deeply grateful for the blessing of plenty, and gave thanks every day that passed. No wonder he became a multi-millionaire.

You would like to be a multi-millionaire? But you think it would be deadly dull having to stick to the truth all the time? You think you would be bored to tears if you had to keep every promise you made.

And the children. Why should **you** concern yourself with other people's kids?

It may sound humdrum to you, but it wasn't to Roy Rogers, who knew how to bring the magic out of his mind. 'Go thou and do likewise.' Don't envy a multi-millionaire. Mimic him.

He was just an exception, you think. Oh no, there are very many millionaires and multi-millionaires who would do all this sort of thing; too many to tell you here. I could write a book about them.

The old order of things, the old world you lived in, must pass away. You have got to **change your thoughts**. If you want big money and all the wonderful things it can bring you, you have got to observe the law of getting – magic follows.

'Can't you bring out the magic in my mind without all that talk of self-denial?' you say. 'Self-sacrifice, purity.'

You don't have to be miserable to be moral.

'I'm always doing something for somebody,' you say; 'chopping wood, carrying coal, running errands, the lot. Hardly anybody says "thank you". I'm a darned fool, mate, and you tell me to go on making sacrifices.'

'I'm not going on with all that nonsense. I've never got anything from anybody, not a carrot from the garden, or an apple off the tree.'

In the world of magic, you don't do things with the idea of somebody giving you something, or saying 'Thank you.' You do things because you genuinely **want** to make people happy without any thought of **what you might get in return**. Once that creeps into it, the magic spell is broken. It won't work. A man must die to his old self and be born again to new ideas.

Money means happiness, and it often means health. The utterly false idea that money creates trouble is a thought conveniently used by those men and women who have no desire to get on in life; hangers-on, who find it easier and more pleasing to sponge on somebody else. Theirs is a lazy mind.

Life should be a dancing thing. But to most people it is not. They have a bit of money in hand and they just manage to come out level at the end of a week or month, and they always seem to be that little bit 'behind' so that they have to spend their days trying desperately, feverishly, to 'catch up'; get straight, make ends meet.

Think of the lives of famous self-made millionaires. Why have they risen above the mass of their fellows?

Men like the late John Rockefeller, Sir Thomas Lipton, and the first Lord Leverhulme became millionaires when the men with whom they spent their boyhood were still in the ranks of workers. What was the secret?

Lipton slept under his counter when he lived in his first little shop in Glasgow. He knew hunger but never complained. Lord Leverhulme and Lord Northcliffe both started with nothing, yet they were never fed up with life.

These men accepted life without a grumble. Boot was penniless when he started. Lever was a traveller, Hartley a grocer, and Bass a carrier. They had scarcely a bean and certainly no influence. But they knew how to bring the magic out of their minds.

Smith's thousands of bookstalls and shops commenced with two brothers who wrapped up newspapers at four o'clock in the morning. (Most of us are asleep!) Whiteley's developed from a ribbon counter, and Pears from a Soho barber who made his own soap.

Then there was the man who made matches as a sideline to blacking. That led to Bryant's success.

The would-be millionaire must be a fanatic, a red-hot flame. These self-made millionaires were all stickers and smilers. They could not see defeat. For wealth they were prepared to show super-optimism, even in the face of seeming failure.

Money has been in the minds of these millionaires all the time; they wanted enough to uplift their spirit, to be free, to be extravagant, to be able to go the limit, to give it away if they wanted to. They made the wilderness blossom like a rose – through magic.

It is not a matter of how you can get more, it is **where are you withholding?** You are here to give to humanity, the law of increase does the rest.

Gypsy Smith told a story of how a man went into business with the determination to put others first. Success came quickly, and he moved into a larger house, saying to his wife, 'For every £500 we spend on our new home, we will spend the same amount on the poor!'

He did that. When the time came that he could afford to spend £1,000 on his home, he gave a similar amount to the poor. He became an amazing success. He had the Midas touch and everything seemed to turn to gold.

Nicolino Alfonso Romano, who was a waiter at the Cafe Royal, bought a fish and chip shop in the Strand and turned it into **his** little restaurant.

'I have staked my all on this,' he said to his solicitor as he waited for men to put the roof on. **Then he commanded his subconscious to bring him good fortune.**

He had the good fortune all right. The actors, gamblers, writers, and sports of Victoria's days went to enjoy themselves at Romano's. The King Edward-to-be took a private room there.

Then the Gaiety girls came with their noble escorts.

When Romano died in 1901 his body was laid in an unclosed coffin upstairs, and the Gaiety girls, the peers, bookmakers, priests, scribes, and jockeys filed past. Romano had had an **astonishing success**, because he let his subconscious take control, and **believed**.

If anybody says to you, 'How the devil can I make more money?' hand him this book. He needs to bring out the magic in his mind.

Once, on the BBC's Billy Cotton's **Wakey, Wakey** show, I put up a £1,000 challenge to four of the leading newspaper television correspondents. In a locked box I placed a cheque for £1,000. In five sealed envelopes I placed five keys. Only one of those keys would open the locked box.

My challenge was this: the correspondents could each choose one of these numbered envelopes – numerals 1 to 5. If one of the keys contained therein would open the box – then the money was for the holder of the key.

You may remember how those shrewd no-nonsense reporters chose their numbers. How I asked them if they would like to change their minds and how only one did.

You may recall that I held envelope number 2 in my hand after the exchange. Then the holders of envelopes 1, 3, 4, and 5 opened their envelopes, extracted their keys, tried to unlock the box – and failed.

After which I opened my number 2 envelope, took out the key, opened the box, and there before the very eyes of the journalist committee on stage was a cheque for £1,000 – **which I retained!**

Magic!

8
The Magic Of Friendship

IF you were to stop any man or woman in the street and ask, 'Have you such a thing as a real intimate friend to whom you can say everything, and from whom you can ask anything?' most of them would probably hesitate before answering, 'Yes, I have.'

Dr Johnson reminds us, 'If a man does not make new acquaintances as he advances through life, he will soon find himself left alone. A man, sir, should keep his friendship in constant repair.'

You can do much to cultivate people and if you want to enjoy life to the full you should have friends in England, and try and have friends in every country. It is grand to be able to say, as someone said to me, 'I have a friend in every country of the world.'

It is one of the tragedies of life that so many friendships which began well, end badly. We grow away from people and often this is sadder than going away from them. There are friends who pass and friends who remain. Few come with us all the way. But when you have qualified as a mental magician, you should know how to keep all your friends, and add new ones as well.

If your friends do not come with you all the way, is it not

nearly always your own fault? Have you not neglected them in some way or other; showed little enthusiasm?

Of course, we all know that friends can tell each other too much, and so spoil what might otherwise have proved a lasting comradeship. It is fun to 'keep something up your sleeve'. You instantly become more fascinating. Mystery lends charm to the personality. Mystery is a part of magic. A magician would never succeed, unless he had plenty of mystery in his act.

And the bores. They are those who lay all their cards on the table at once; giving themselves away in every detail. It is not good psychology to tell one's story at a sitting, when the story which excites the most, whether in fiction or life, is the story which finishes at the spot where you want it to go on. Be tactful. Refrain from speaking unkind words.

I can remember how once at a club meeting, people kept standing up in turns, saying something unkind about one of the characters in the room.

One particular man had listened the whole evening without a murmur, but at the end of it all he stood up in defence of the criticized one, and gave the back-biting conversation a kindly twist. He was different from the rest.

'Don't say **that**.' he explained. 'I think he has been splendid, and anyhow . . .'

Somehow it struck me as rather fine. Certainly I should like all my friends to be like that. Friends who thought so well of you that they could not bear to hear you ill-spoken of; so sensitive to what appeared to them your shining merits that they defended you at the first signs of reproach. It is a lovely thing to be perfectly loyal to a friend.

There are rare friendships, like that of David and Jonathan, which flare magically into being because there is something in each that strikes a spark of spontaneous appreciation. Dante said of Beatrice, 'Whensoever she appeared before me, I had no enemy left on earth; the flame of charity kindled within me, caused me to forgive all who had ever offended me.'

Always find something fresh to admire and appreciate in the object of your affection, and tell them so! Compliment again and again. Be grateful for friendships. You begin to make friends with a person when you begin to make sacrifices. You sacrifice your thoughts and your time, and some of your money. You dream of how you will give and devote yourself to that friend. And you do. The friendship remains as long as the sacrifices continue; as long as you are prepared to 'do something'. And ask something of your friends; if they are not 'used' now and again, they do not think you care for them.

To offer someone you love the gift of friendship, you must give what is wanted of you, **and no more**. And having gained their affection, you must **follow up** and **follow through** to make that friendship vital and lasting. You must do things to keep the comradeship alive.

Two friends have been jogging along through the years not noticing that they were getting older, then something happens that jars them into the realization that they are no longer as young as they used to be when life was fun.

It throws them into a panic.

It makes them feel that they are missing something. They have been too busy trying to make a fortune to have much gaiety together. They have always been **going to**. They let their chance of a good time together slip by, then suddenly they wake up to the fact that it is nearly all over. You must never be like that. There is magic in friendship when you can continue the fun right through to old age together.

You have **not had time** to write letters to each other, been too busy to 'phone. It is always 'I'm in a tremendous hurry, my dear,' nobody knows what for!

Suddenly you begin to feel as one does during the last dance of a ball, tired but keen, and you decide to make the most of each bar of music before you must go home.

It is then that you turn instinctively and lovingly to the friends who are left. You talk about the **good old days** when you let yourselves go and painted the town red. You have those disturbing moments at eventide when you feel a little mean, and a little dirty. Days of haste in word and deed. The worst in you has conquered. Dear one hurt. You wish you had been different.

You **can** be different. You can think of these things during meditation and determine to do something about it. Your subconscious will guide you and tell you what to do to keep your friends as keen as they were in the beginning.

Someone said to me, 'I did not know how to make friends. I would see people whom I thought would make wonderful friends, but I did not know how to approach them.'

There came a day when that person lay in hospital, and those who wanted so much to become her friend came forward to offer love and sympathy. One visit, and they came again and again.

'I suppose it must sound foolish,' she said, 'but I am glad it happened. I never knew before how lovely people could be. I did not know anyone could be loved as much as people seemed to love me. They were all so kind. Perhaps if I had made the first step, they would have been only too glad to welcome me into their little circle.'

Travelling from London to Manchester by train, a man shared his carriage with only one other man. Neither spoke. Both wanted to.

Their train arrived, they rose, collected their hats, over-coats, and suitcases, and made a simultaneous dash for the door. Of course, they stuck. And then one man spoke. 'Pair of fools, what?' he grinned. 'Like to have a chat with you sometime. So long.'

Unless there are introductions, nobody seems pleased to see anybody else and it is particularly noticeable in railway carriages.

You must have friends. **Get out more. Mix more freely.** Meet other people, widen your interests.

If you are lonely, don't think that you must necessarily

receive friendship. **Give** it. Don't hold back. Give of yourself to others. Do something, do it for others. Loneliness is not a physical state, but a **mental** state. You can feel desperately lonely in a crowd.

I once saw a framed motto on the wall of a guest room. **I am part of all that I have met,** it said. But I know that it can also mean, **and a part of me belongs to those I meet.**

We **are** a part of everyone we meet.

You must feel and think yourself a friend, and go one step further and actually **see** yourself as already a friend. Your subconscious will assimilate this and then go about its own way to work the magic of friendship for you. Whatever your subconscious urges you to do towards making the friend, do it **immediately.** So many people have a negative outlook about making friends. If the sun shines today, it will rain tomorrow. They go through life expecting the worst all the time. If you tell your subconscious that a certain person will snub you rather than welcome you as a friend, then it won't be any good. **The subconscious works to your dictation,** it gives you exactly what you expect.

You can go from one glorious friendship to another, if you talk to your subconscious in the right way. Friendships that can help you attain your wildest dreams. But you must be positive in your attitude. The magic word is **attitude.** You can have top-class friends, friends to be proud of, and the doubting Thomases will say, 'Well, well, he wasn't such a fool after all.'

It is the **belief** within you that brings results. The essential of success or making grand friends is that your desire must be an all-obsessing one. Whatever you want, make that thing or that person your magnificent obsession. The way to work magic in getting friends is unknown to the majority of people. Many people would **give anything** to know what I'm telling you in this book. You can have the best friends anybody ever had.

You must realize that people may be genuinely delighted

101

to see you, but may not have the time or inclination to develop a closer friendship yet awhile. It takes time with some people. People can be pleased to see you often without necessarily wishing to become bosom friends all at once. You must not be hurt or annoyed with these types, but understanding. It is no use thinking that everybody should be specially nice to you because you live alone, or are lonely.

To make friends you have to see a person regularly and often and, above all, make yourself of use to them. Give garden shears to a man who is without them, offer to baby-sit if you know a young couple who cannot get out together. If you have a car, take a sick or tired man for a drive in the country, or give a lift into town to someone you know and see waiting at the bus stop. Little kindnesses work magic in the cultivation of friendships. Be more interested in the other person than in yourself, and have the grace never to show boredom if the other fellow talks too much. Service to others is the most important thing to remember. Your circle of friends will widen with each kind act.

You must have friends, preferably friends in every country, so that your subconscious can tap, tap, tap them to your advantage.

Distance has ceased to have any meaning, whatever region of the world you occupy, you are neighbours now.

Why not invite the lady next door in for a cup of tea? Why not ask the man in the flat below to come and share your television? When did you last speak to them? Ask if they've had their holiday, where they are going or where they have been. Talk only of pleasant things. Is there somebody you should be caring about? Think. Surely not your mother?

'And now it's too late. . . .' These can be sad words, words that are said when someone you love has died or gone away. You begin to think of all that you might have done. Face the fact that you can never get time back. Always remember that and be loving and patient now. Remorse is an awful thing.

Recently a man jumped under a train and killed himself. He left a note behind him saying he was torn by **remorse**. That was why he had done it. He could not get it off his mind; the things he **could** have done, but it was **too late**.

When the winter snows came, neighbours who had preserved a cold indifference to each other for months, sometimes years, broke the ice and had a word with each other, even gave each other warming drinks. You could say, like the men in the railway carriage said: 'Fools, weren't we?'

Once, when Sophie Tucker flew into London she took a suite at the Savoy Hotel, but decided that the suite was on the small side. She wanted to entertain.

'I've got friends, and when you've got friends you just **have** to throw parties,' she said. The Savoy saw to it that this red-hot momma was moved into a bigger suite.

The rooms were like a bower of flowers and good-luck messages were piled high on the writing-desk.

'Every one of these will be replied to by the time I go to bed tonight,' she said. 'I refuse to have a secretary. I write every letter myself. 'When you got friends, pal, you gotta give, see.' Sophie Tucker knows how to be a friend all right. **'You gotta give, see!'**

Giving, and preferring to give, is the magic that brings friends.

It's sad how many people shy off the idea of having anyone into their home. They even boast that they 'keep themselves to themselves'.

This attitude is all wrong. It is negative. Anyone who thinks like this must never expect to work magic. If we do not get to know, and generally befriend our neighbours, how are we going to meet people and make new friends?

Mention the work entertaining, and some people imagine an elaborate dinner party like you read about in the glossy magazines. It is not necessary. A cup of tea or coffee, a drink of beer or wine, is quite enjoyable when you meet for a chat. But I will say this, that when you have mastered what I have been saying, you will want to give elaborate dinner parties, you will want to dress for dinner, because you will have raised your standard of living and like attracts like. You will give them, and be given them, in this new life of luxury that magic will bring.

The waste of life lies in the love we have not given, the powers we have not used. It is the stinginess of spirit that wears us out; the anxiety lest we give more than we receive. This destroys us. The way to work magic with friendship is to go beyond the minimum requirements of friendship. The surplus effort, the overflowing of the cup of joy, the doing of the undemanded deed, is what puts magnetism into us, and attracts the things we want. Entertaining at home is a lovely way to get to know people. You should take a great interest in others to encourage friendship. 'Was your trip a success?' shows that you have the other person's happiness at heart. 'Did you enjoy the party?' shows you are really interested in the other person's life. Ask only questions of general interest. Do not pry into private affairs, that is the easiest way to part company.

Live to help others and forge friendships with them. Simply opening a door for someone to pass through is an expression of friendship.

The more you live to help others in the overcoming of their obstacles, the more certain you are of solving your own. You are purifying yourself with every unselfish action, and purification lifts you to the highest plane where you are able to get real guidance.

You can talk, even if the stranger is a woman. You don't greet her with the words, 'Say, what time is your husband coming home?'; you may get a slap on the face for your impudence. You are riding for a fall like that. But say, 'What beautiful scenery, isn't it?' or 'Isn't it a glorious day?' If you are at a concert, for instance, you can say, 'What beautiful music, isn't it?' And she will respond.

I like the words of Shakespeare. 'But if the while I think

on thee, dear friend, all losses are restored and sorrow end.'
Sorrows can end or be made easier to bear when friends
share and comfort each other.

Friendship brings out the magic. It has been there in your
mind all the time, but in a deep freeze. Suddenly you meet
someone, and you know instinctively he or she is your kind
of person.

A friend of mine from sunny Australia remarked how
blank everyone here looks. And someone from South Africa
was positively amazed at the lack of radiance he saw on the
faces of the English people. In Italy, Spain, and Mexico a
face is an instrument of expression. As a great novelist said,
'Whole sonatas are played on it, by its excitable possessor.'

You should have a smile for everybody. Your gay infectious
spirits and wonderful charm (which I hope you will get from
reading this book) will attract people to you. You will be a
'new and exciting' you.

Make friends with actors and actresses who thrill you on
the stage and television, drop a line of appreciation to the
authors who write books you admire, or books that have
helped you. Write to those who give you pleasure over the
radio, in newspapers and magazines.

People won't come knocking on your door pleading to be
a friend! You must make friends yourself in every possible
way you can.

A miner once told me in a burst of confidence what he
thought of a certain well-known actor:

'There's nothing high-hat about that feller,' he said, 'like
a lot of these famous men. Why, brother, this bird hobnobs
with them men, not like he was patronizing 'em, y'understand,
but like he likes 'em. And believe me, they like him, too.'

Ever watched one of those films in which the men bang
each other on the back with a strangled cry of 'Buddy'?

We like to think of our best friend like that. True as steel,
staunch as a lion, faithful unto death.

A famous film star who was one of the sincerest people

you could ever come across, said that if there was anything he disliked, it was insincerity in any form.

'I think the thing that gets my goat quicker than anything else is to have someone come gushing up to me and say, "Why, old man, how are you? I'm so glad to see you again. What have you been doing with yourself?" and then when I answer, either he's turned away to say "Howdy!" to someone else, or if he's still standing there, he's not listening to me, but looking around to see who else is there. It makes you feel that they don't really give a tinker's damn about you, after all.'

Pay attention and always be nice. It reminds me of a true story. Fans turned out in force when Frank Sinatra was booked by an Atlantic City night club. One girl stood outside Sinatra's hotel two days waving a placard that said, **I adore Frank Sinatra.**

Sinatra paid no attention to her.

On the third day the girl's placard read, 'You've had your chance. **I adore Elvis.**'

See what I mean?

Jane Austen, who created the novel based on character instead of action, makes a figure in one of her books say of another:

'You never see a fault in anybody. All the world are good and agreeable in your eyes. I never heard you speak ill of a human being in my life . . . to take the good of everybody's character and make it still better, and say nothing of the bad, belongs to you alone.'

This is how we should all be.

And this is a war story. When the remnant got back to their trenches, one boy discovered that his pal was missing. He asked his officer if he might go out into no-man's-land to look for him.

The officer said, 'Yes, you may go, but it isn't worth it.'

The boy went, and in a little time returned mortally wounded.

Before he died he said to his officer, 'It was worth it, sir, for when I reached him he said, "I knew you'd come." '

That is friendship. Real friendship.

Many friends travel with us only to the crossroads and then, whether the farewell be conscious or unconscious, we turn in different directions.

What a tragedy. Yet it seems to happen in the lives of every one of us. It does not always prove disloyalty or failure, it means that we are in the grip of different tendencies and circumstances. Destiny would seem to bear us east and west. We must guard against this as much as we can.

You have friends. I have friends. The man next door has friends; watch him trot off to the golf club any Saturday morning.

Let us try to keep what friends we have, for what a treasure beyond compare it is to have at least one friend who has been with us throughout a lifetime.

Have I achieved what it takes to be a friend? I hope so. The **Halifax Daily Courier and Guardian,** September 6th, 1957, speaks of me as:

'. . . on stage and before the camera, a slick, self-assured mental magician; off-stage, a comfortable, COMFORTING and unassuming man.'

And in **The Irish Times,** September 18th, 1956:

'Al Koran, who is reading minds at the Theatre Royal this week, is a quiet young man with prematurely grey hair, A GENTLE MANNER, a soft, hesitant voice, and eyes which could almost be described as starry. . . .'

9
The Magic Of Change

MAGIC means **change**. You change one thing into another. The Great Psychologist turned water into wine and that was magic.

Change is what you want. You want prosperity instead of the endless struggle for money. You want to be Somebody, and do something great. Everybody wants to be important. You want beauty instead of ugliness; champagne instead of beer; a Rolls instead of a bicycle; a mansion instead of a flat. You would like a palace if you could get it.

Yes, you want to work magic; magic is what changes the drab into the lovely; the ordinary into the extraordinary.

How do you set about it? You change **yourself** first. Change your way of thinking; change your attitude to life altogether. It is a thing you can only do for yourself. Nobody else can do it for you. I can show you the way, but it's **you** who have to work the magic.

Perhaps there are not many books that might change your life. But this one will if you take it as gospel. Don Quixote wrote romantic tales of valour, tales about a knight, and he became a knight himself. Reading books sent Don Quixote on his travels; and this book may send you on the most exciting journey of your life.

John Bunyan read the Bible, and became one of our greatest English authors. Who knows, **your** turning-point in life might be brought about by reading all this. I hope so.

Take heed, then, the whole idea of magic is **change.**

It pays to change. Make no mistake about it. You have been content to jog along accepting a minimum existence. **You** must be different. **All great men and women are different;** different to the masses, and that is what brings them magic.

You must have enough guts to rebel against having a dull life. There is an art in being different; in changing. It does not mean that you have to irritate your family, your wife, your husband, as the case may be, only that you claim the right to speak and act as you feel. And from now on, you are going to think, speak, and act in a **positive** way.

Are you 'fed up' at the end of the day; worn out and bad-tempered? If you are, **and you don't change,** you've 'had it'. You must change, and change quickly, or this worn-out feeling will increase.

The truth is, you are 'fed up' with doing the same things day after day, though you may not realize it. Nothing can be more tiring than seeing the same faces every day, hearing the same bits of advice like 'Cheer up, old man' from the hearties. You are 'fed up' with catching the same bus or train day in and day out. 'Fed up' with putting the cats out, and trying to get the cats in! 'Fed up' with shopping and waiting in queues.

What you need is a change, and freedom to do as you please. You must get it.

You want 'something to happen'. Something nice. To work, to sleep, to eat, to work, and to sleep again – that way madness lies.

'They must often **change** who would be constant in happiness,' wrote Confucius, and Bacon backed up this statement with the words, 'Nothing is pleasant that is not spiced with variety.'

Start with little changes. Go shopping or to work by a different route. This means that you will see a fresh set of faces, different buildings, even the ticket which has been buff may be suddenly transformed to green or blue. Eat out if you usually eat in. Eat in if you usually eat out. Read your paper from back to front. Use your left hand instead of your right. **Determine to smash routine.**

There was a person once who said to President Roosevelt, 'Something interesting is always happening to you.' He answered, 'I take good care that it does.'

To most people life is a drab affair. They are bored. They will tell you everything is the same. **But everything need not be the same!**

To sleep in the same bed every night, eat from the same table, favour the same pastimes without care or thought for the jostling crowd. **That is complete madness.**

Couldn't you sleep in a different bed in another room, for a change? Couldn't you eat from another table once in a while? If you play golf or tennis regularly, couldn't you go boating or fly a kite now and again?

You will always find that the people who live in a vicious circle (doing the same thing, in the same way, week after week, year after year) are the people who are always next door to nervous exhaustion, today, tomorrow, and every day.

Don't be a slave to **sameness.** 'Pull yourself together,' people say. How you wish you could.

Get yourself a diary, and each day write in it something new and different which you have done on that day. Like this you have a constant reminder and can get yourself out of the rut.

If you had to get up at five o'clock in the morning and walk a mile and a half to the bank to cash a cheque for a hundred pounds, you would do it like a shot! Tiredness would not enter into it. You would be up with the lark and off like a streak of forced lightning!

You are tired and exhausted simply because you are absolutely fed up with things. There is no spirit of adventure in what you are doing. It is all the same. The man who goes

110

away to the seaside and paddles with the kiddies for a fortnight, feels fine and says the sea has done him good.

It has to a certain extent, but it is the **change** from the eternal sameness of every day which has worked magic.

You must change your pattern of life. But make the **right** patterns.

Once you become satisfied with things as they are, you have ceased to thrill at the chance of a new adventure, the best of life is over.

Try something new every now and again, every day if you can. You have been used to seeing a musical show – buy a ticket for a new play instead. Or go to a first night, if you have never been used to doing this.

Go and see all the magicians you can. 'I've seen him before,' you might say, but go again. Magicians change their programmes. Take the Magical Claudine. This dark-haired lovely lady appeared in satin tails, and included a beautiful dog in her act of magic. Now she appears with blonde hair, and a glamorous white dress, and quite a different set of magical equipment. Magicians know the value of **change**. You must know it too.

Determine to get more out of life. Make every day exciting ('What can I make happen now?') Do something to make life fuller, richer, deeper, broader, different – so that it can never become dull.

Turn places upside down. Do not cling to one style all the time. A husband told me the other day that his wife was always changing around the furniture. He would come home, and everything would be in a different place. Well, that wife at least has the know-how of magic. She will never get in a rut. Neither will she let her husband get bored with sameness.

Alter everything. Do opposite to what you did before. Things which have stood in certain places for years can be found another place. Leave not one thing as it used to be.

Then set about yourself. Get a new frock in a new style, or order a different kind of suit. Alter the dressing of your

111

hair, even the colour if you want to. Try out new foods. Cook in a new way.

You will become a new personality. You will feel and look ten years younger. Do not get into a rut that is too deep to climb out of; too deep to be able to see over the top.

The famous actress Jackie Collins says: 'Oh, for sure, I changed all of me.' She realized she was in a rut and did something about it.

'Jackie Collins,' she said, scowling at herself in the mirror, 'you look horrible.' What did she do?

She decided to change everything about her. 'You've got to change your face, your figure, your life – the lot!' she said.

She had her nose changed by plastic surgery. She was plump and she slimmed her figure. She had her hair tinted red and turned it up instead of wearing it long. She changed her agent, and changed her food. She even changed her name. Now she was Lynn Curtis. She has gone from one success to another, and life is exciting.

Take Douglas Fairbanks Jnr, who has always looked a very British gentleman. He hired a New York public relations firm to make him look more American (he is American by birth). Douglas wants to project himself as an all-American corporation executive, as he thinks it a disadvantage that so many Americans think of him as British.

Anthony Glyn, author of the famous novel **I can Take it All**, decided one day to **change**, and his wife decided that she was happy to go along with him over this.

'First I changed my appearance completely,' she said. 'I sold all my clothes, those faultless little brown, grey, or navy dresses. And I got myself some **scarlet jeans.** I do my hair Spanish style now, and I wear shorts in summer. I'd never worn shorts in my life before.

'When I was first married we went to Paris for our honeymoon and I fussed terribly over my clothes – little black hats and dresses, very much milady abroad. But we went back in our new personalities. I went in jeans and a football jersey, and carried a string bag of lemons, because I like the colour, and we went to little cafés and night clubs. It was much more fun.

'Our great idea, you see, was **to give up things that bore us**'.

Sir Anthony and Lady Glyn have **new personalities** and declare they are enjoying life more since they **changed**.

Are you always tired? Could you drop off – anywhere? You need a **change**. This thought has breath-taking possibilities. Try it.

I was looking at a magazine the other day and read: 'Every night for four years my wife has eaten two rounds of bread and blackcurrant jam washed down by half a pint of cocoa.' Four years. See what I mean?

Thumbing through another magazine: **Perplexed wife, at dinner table, to angry husband: 'Monday you liked beans, Tuesday you liked beans, Wednesday you liked beans. Now, all of a sudden, on Thursday you don't like beans!'** Meant to be funny, but there is a lot of truth in it. There are people who each day breakfast in the same way – the same spoon, the same plate, the same kind of marmalade from year to year. Magic never comes to them. They haven't a clue.

Do you eat outside in the summer? There's no doubt about it, eating on the terrace gives you a more exotic, sun-drenched Mediterranean feeling if you do it in style – **different** china, **different** linen, **different** food from the year-in year-out familiar friends.

We all know people in a vicious circle, though they may not realize themselves that they are in it. The neighbour whose garden gate clicks at the same moment every morning. You could set your watch by it, so exact is he doing the same thing at precisely the same time every day. You know the night he takes his wife to the cinema, and the night they stay at home for television. You know the exact moment old Brown across the way takes Rusty the airedale for a run, the exact time the Smiths turn out the light and go to bed.

And there is the spinster you know who goes to the same cottage every year and sends the same picture postcards to the same set of friends. Year in. Year out. And so on for the rest of life.

Such a fate is dreadful. Anything, any change, rather than one long eternal sameness.

Whatever you do, do not get into a rut. Vary the formula of your work and life. Strike out along new paths once in a while. Sameness, mere routine, in the long run spells decay.

I knew a woman who always wore heavy tweeds and thick brogues. Someone gave her a lace handkerchief for Christmas, and she **changed**. She became more feminine; wore high-heel shoes, velvets, satins, and gossamer undies. Her whole personality became vibrant, gay, and exciting.

Get out of the rut. **Change.** Get out! All ruts are bad, even those that are lined with rose leaves. Put on your hat and go! Go anywhere. See anything. Look for the unexpected.

There are men and women I knew years ago who are still just as charming; just as pretty. **But the fire has gone out.** They wanted at one time to throw their arms around everybody, they felt so happy, so alive. They wanted to shout for joy, till the stars came tumbling down through the roof.

But now they will say, 'I have longed again and again for that moment. I do not know what it was, but to me it never comes again.'

It is such a pity. Most everyone has such an experience in a lifetime. To perpetuate this state, you must **try something new**, you must **make a change** and so stir that within you which readily responds with pep to the thrill of a joyful surprise.

The one vital factor in all things that get on our nerves is **repetition**. It is the constant repetition of something we dislike to hear or see or do which kills; kills the gay, ever-young spirit within us.

I change my performances quite often. I **change** the clothes I wear on the stage; sometimes a velvet jacket, sometimes just an ordinary suit. And I've **changed** my name – from Al Koran to KORAN

Change brings magic.

114

10
The Magic Of Charms And Mascots

ARE charms really lucky? Do mascots bring success? The answer is – **if you believe.** A magician, if he is a real psychologist, can make these things work magic. It depends entirely upon **belief.** Perhaps theatrical people, rather more than most people, have strong beliefs. They will carry charms, and put mascots on their dressing-table, and somehow – it works. It is, of course, the amount of belief that they have put into that one particular thing. In it they have centred all their faith, and because of this, the charm or mascot responds.

I believe in charms and mascots, because I think that most people need something in which to believe. It is a childish idea, but then, we have to become as little children, for that way happiness and success comes to us.

Shirley Bassey, the well-known stage and television singer, had a **big kiss** for her bizarre mascot at London airport when she arrived back from Milan some little while ago. That is the sort of thing a child would do, but it makes the mascot something **real** to her, and as psychologists, we know that **feeling** counts. It is the most important thing with regard to working magic. You must **feel** that it will. We all know that Shirley is tremendously successful.

A mascot is something on which we pin our faith, and it is a very good thing to have a point of concentration like this. It is practised in hypnotism. You are given a central point to concentrate upon, then after a while you are able to perform things you could never have done before. Mascots are a great help inasmuch as they get you into the habit of having a focal point to meditate upon, and the more your mind is centred on one particular spot, the more strong does it become. It is when you waver about in your mind that nothing happens.

Donald Campbell, the record-breaking water and land speed champion, who has broken his own fantastic records many times, always takes **Woppit** with him; the fastest water-borne bear in the world. The bear stands eight inches high and has brilliant green ears and feet and wears a red waistcoat. '**Woppit** goes everywhere with me,' says Donald. The little bear is his lucky mascot. And how lucky Donald has been. With **Woppit** he has tremendous courage.

Another man of courage is Stan Stennett, the well-known comedian. He has his own little aeroplane and loves flying. As a keen amateur pilot, it is perhaps only natural that he should keep as his mascot something connected with flying. He has a model aeroplane that he made himself and takes it with him on any flights he makes and on theatrical engagements when he uses his personal aircraft – a four-seater **Cessna**. He treasures his mascot, believes in it, and fills the theatre wherever he appears.

Ken Dodd the stage comedian, who so often has his own show on television, puts all his faith in a lucky sixpence his mother gave to him years ago. 'Whenever I begin a new radio or TV series or open in a big show for a season, I always carry in the pocket of my suit the sixpence my mother gave to me,' he says. Ken is a brilliant success.

Let me give you a few more instances, before we talk about charms. Terry Hall, the ventriloquist behind television's popular Lenny the Lion, has a mascot. Terry, through the lovable lion, makes millions laugh. 'Most people believe,

116

quite understandably, that my lucky mascot is Lenny the Lion,' he says. 'I suppose that this is true, to some extent, but the object which I personally regard as my lucky mascot is a small miniature lamp. This was the first gift I ever received from a fan of Lenny the Lion,' he went on. 'It arrived after Lenny's first TV appearance when, during the programme, I mentioned that Lenny had his own room at home and always slept in the dark. Since then, of course, he has had a lamp. It came from a little girl who pointed out that she wanted Lenny to have the lamp so that he would no longer have to sleep in the dark.'

Rather sweet, don't you think?

'I take it around in Lenny's case whenever we have a theatrical engagement, and it arouses great interest when visitors see it on my dressing-table.'

Terry with Lenny the Lion has achieved wonderful success, and makes a lot of money. It seems that all those with a mascot achieve success, doesn't it? You see, they have something to concentrate upon, hoping it will bring them luck. Almost a command to the subconscious, isn't it?

One woman laughed so much she nearly fell off her seat, when Gordon Peters, the comedian, was on the stage. 'My mascot is a little wooden Mickey Mouse,' he says, 'with one leg on a scooter. He was given to me during a pantomime season, on the last night. He always goes with me, even to the Middle East. I put him on my dressing-table. He is a funny-looking little fellow and makes you smile to look at him. But I am sure he brings me luck; I always play to packed houses.'

Terence Rattigan, the famous playwright, has always had the golden touch. He has written many successful plays and films, and knows what it is like to have big money. Terence likes to keep the champagne corks from the first-night celebration of his play. One could go on naming hundreds of famous personalities who believe in mascots, and who have plenty of luck.

117

The late W. Macqueen-Pope, famous theatre historian, admitted that he always carried a whole waistcoat pocket full of mascots with him – he would not move without them.

Do inanimate objects have power? One would think not, but remember what I said about the engine-room of the liner, how when it had broken down and nobody could make it go, it went when it was spoken to nicely? The same applies to a man with a car; it will go well for some people and not for others. Maybe it is the thought they send out to it, just as it is with mascots.

Some people prefer rings. That well-known personality Benny Hill never appears without the small diamond ring his father gave him for his 21st birthday. He believes in it bringing him luck.

It would be futile to wear such a ring and put no trust in it. Cardinal Wolsey possessed a magic ring, it is said, which aided him in his climb to eminence in the Church. Nicholas II of Russia put great faith in a fragment of the True Cross which he had on his finger in a ring. This he had left behind him on the day of his assassination. Television star Diane Todd wears an outsize topaz ring. 'There's a story behind it,' she says. She bought it when she went to Majorca for a holiday. She was searching for one to add to her collection, but they were all too large, so she almost ignored the ring she saw in a small shop window. But something made her go in, and the ring fitted perfectly.

'This ring,' the shopkeeper promised her, 'will bring you luck.'

It did. She won many big parts and appears in numerous television programmes.

She thought the luck had faded when her father was taken very seriously ill. But she wore the ring when she went along to see him in hospital, and his recovery was so remarkable that the hospital staff called him The Miracle Man.

Ann Todd, the stage and film star, has a bangle with masses

of charms on it, and she always wears it for luck. Rosalind Russell, the star, wears a bangle of charms she collected when she played in the Broadway show 'Auntie Mame'. 'It tinkles like a cow bell,' she says. 'It's heavy; I list slightly to port whenever I wear it.' The charms are a perfume flask, a lipstick case, telephone pad, whistle, gold mesh purse, pencil, and an antique cigar-cutter. She believes they are all lucky for her. 'I wore the bracelet to a friend's home for dinner,' she said. Later the friend called and said, 'I hope you will excuse the butler coming in and out of the room so often. Every time you moved he thought we had rung the dinner bell!'

That's how keen some people are to carry their charms with them. We all know how lucky Rosalind has been.

For centuries travellers to Tibet have been told that the great wealth and power of the Tibetan families is attributed to a Talli charm so powerful that it draws money like a magnet. The charms were guarded fiercely. Talli himself was fabulously lucky in money matters, rather like Midas for whom everything he touched turned to gold. An Indian Rajah is said to have offered £250,000 for the original Talli charm, but was laughed to scorn. The ancients put great faith in charms and talismans.

You can do the same, whatever charm you choose to have. Give it power with your love and concentration. How deeply do you believe? Once you can believe, you can draw good luck to you. You can magnetize your charm with your own belief.

History shows that to the Greeks and Romans all rings had a profound significance. Legend and fable give us many instances in the power of certain rings.

Frank Crew, the well-known author and columnist, believes in a serpent ring. The serpent, he will tell you, symbolizes renovation and healing. It is said that when old it has the power of growing young again, and gives this same power to its wearer.

The serpent, in reality, or as an emblem, was sacred to

119

Aesculapius, the Greek god of medicine, as it was supposed to have the power of discovering healing herbs, which is why two serpents appear in the badge of the Royal Army Medical Corps.

And it is the symbol of wisdom. Frank Crew will remind you that an author must have wisdom! 'Be ye therefore wise as serpents, and harmless as doves' (Matt. x. 16).

A serpent is said to give power in **seeing into the future.** Can Frank see into the future? you may ask. I have met Frank Crew but once when he came to interview me backstage, and he was gleaning information from me rather than imparting it himself. But I was quick to recognize that he was a man with some extra-sensory perception. It is unnecessary for me to say how I recognized this; it is just as natural for me to glimpse it in people as it may be for you to like or dislike instantly some of the people whom you meet. It was when his eyes lighted upon the ring I was wearing that he came to speak of what the serpent meant to him. In point of fact, the serpent has been of great significance in the Crew family for hundreds of years. Frank Crew's family crest is a greyhound with a serpent entwined. The family motto is: **In Altiora,** which very simply translated means **The Highest.**

To Frank, the serpent which seems to dominate the greyhound is something to which he is always looking up. This brings me back to what I said at the beginning; a mascot or a charm can be very helpful to you if you use it as a focal point of concentration. He told me in a few short minutes that he scorned the idea of the careless, haphazard thought that charms bring luck without the effort of their owners towards attainment. I could judge very well that his ideals, his ambitions, his very thoughts, were a translation of those Latin words **In Altiora – The Highest,** which were inscribed underneath the engraving of the greyhound with the serpent entwined.

We may not all have serpents in our family crests, we may not all wear serpent rings, but many of us, privately or publicly, may be the possessor of some charm or mascot which we believe is a luck bringer.

If you have a charm or mascot, I suggest to you that its potentiality can be greatly increased by your added concentration upon it. You don't want to be haphazard about it. You don't want merely to put some trinket or medalion in your pocket, on your wrist or neck, and carelessly leave it to do the rest. You must, I repeat, **believe** in what it can do, and **believe** in your power to magnetize it. In effect, you don't say, 'This little gold key is going to give me all I want,' you must say, 'With this little gold key I am going to get all I want.' Think well upon it. Hold it, whatever it may be, warmly in your grasp. Wear it if you want to, close to your heart. Have it anywhere you choose, but be **aware** of it all the time. Concentrate on it as Frank Crew, so it appears to me, concentrates on **the highest**, to which the serpent seems a signpost.

Do you remember what I said in an earlier chapter about the importance of meditation? Now that I have explained to you the power with which you can infuse your charm, make it an opportunity to go into the silence, take out your mascot or charm, and set it up in front of you at the commencement of your meditation. You will learn to laugh at all those who may scoff at you for being superstitious. You will have learned how to use it. They won't learn. That is the diff...

I am never without a ... his ring is of solid gold with ... of the zodiac appear in gold ... to it, and regard it as very lu... for me.

A short time ago a famo... d suicide, asked me to sell it ... y to that elusive quality – pe... No amount of money woul... or even go without wearing ... the magnetism of my body. ... piece of jewellery; **it is part o**...

11
The Magic Of Right Impressions

You are digging. If the spade goes well in at the first impression up comes a good clean spadeful. **It is the first impression that counts.**

You are swimming. It is the first push off that takes you half-way across the bath.

You are writing. A good first paragraph makes all the difference to your story.

A good first impression has often helped the wise person who made it to fortune.

On meeting people for the first time, it is our clothes, rather than our personality, which makes the stronger impression. What we wear strikes a good or bad note, and gives people an index to our character and position in life.

Right clothes are Might. They spell Power. That is why the Lord Chief Justice wears upon his learned head the bleached hair of the horse. That is why he wraps himself up in the fur of the wild beasts. **It is to impress us.**

You must impress the world with your importance if you would be a success, and if you would work magic. The world sums you up by the clothes you wear, and treats you accordingly. If you are not dressed beautifully, nobody can think you are a magician. Shabbiness not only denotes carelessness,

122

but a depressed and morbid mental outlook. You, as a magician, want to show that your mental outlook is stupendous.

The bus conductor who gives you your ticket sizes you up by the sort of attire you have on. So do railway officials, theatre and cinema attendants, and employers who have advertised a vacant position.

Do you look like a person who knows how to get everything you want? Do you look like a person who understands magic?

Does your wife dress beautifully? Is she your trade-mark; your sign of prosperity? Nothing can advertise a man's success as a smartly-clad up-to-date wife.

Impress the world with the thought that **only the best is good enough for you.**

'The best is good enough for me,' said the late Arnold Bennett. 'Give me the best and I shall be satisfied.'

When you deliberately claim only the best in life you know what you want, and you get it, because you have become a specialist in the art of magic. When the best becomes an essential thing to you, you are willing to work for it. You are willing to visualize. You are willing and eager to talk to your subconscious. And having made the best your claim in life, you know a good thing when you see it, and you recognize good people. **The best** becomes automatically labelled upon you for all time. People see you, and are at once sure that you know the secret of magic.

A famous comedian once wrote in his autobiography: 'Never let it appear that you are hard up. When I have had hunger gnawing at my stomach like a ruthless wolf, I have always pretended the whole world was at my beck and call. I have always pretended that luck was on my side. I have gone about well-dressed, sporting silk shirts, patent leather shoes, and fur on my coat, carrying an ebony walking stick with a silver handle, like any toff, even buying a car, though it meant going without food to do it.'

This man was a clown, but he was not a fool. 'Have a good impression of yourself,' he wrote in his book. 'Ask terms that simply make your partner sweat with horror. At rock-bottom it is an artist's salary that makes his reputation. Have a cock-sureness and unwavering faith in your career-to-be that are proof against all reproach.'

He created the impression of success, even when he was down and out, but that impression, together with faith in himself, brought him great fame and fortune.

I would like to tell you the story of a certain physician who was rapidly making his way in his profession. He sold his old car, a small saloon, and bought a leading make of limousine.

His friends told him he was extravagant, as the added cost of maintaining this car would be at least £500 a year. But the physician, after a little while, said that the new car had paid for itself handsomely. It set a good impression. It was the best.

And as a direct result of driving about in such a magnificent car, the physician experienced an immense increase in his practice which more than paid for the added cost. Everybody regarded the new car as evidence that he was a very successful man.

There is a similar story about an Englishman who came back from Hollywood where he had been writing screen stories.

For months when he first went out he haunted the studios trying to get interviews with prominent people, but he was always put off on some pretext or other.

He was complaining one day of his bad luck to a friend who had been in Hollywood for some time.

'Have you a car?' said the friend.

'No,' replied the Englishman. 'What has that got to do with it?'

'Buy one and see,' said the other.

Next day, on borrowed money, the Englishman bought a smart scarlet two-seater. He had another appointment that afternoon, and went in his car to keep it. To his surprise he was admitted immediately, and was successful in getting a contract for several screen stories.

'They won't see you unless you drive up in a car,' his friend told him afterwards. 'They look on the man who hasn't a car as a failure.'

Life is like that. 'To him that hath shall be given,' so **appear as if you have**. Appear successful. Appear as though you are the one who knows how to work magic.

There was a girl patient at St Thomas's Hospital, London, who had been bedridden for four years and finally sent home because she failed to respond to treatment.

But before she left the hospital a Ladies' Guild provided her with some nice new clothes. **The effect was magical.** In a few weeks' time she walked into the hospital well and happy. It was the tonic of new clothes. She felt successful.

Beautiful clothes matter tremendously. One wears them to make a success of things. The peacock does not flaunt its tail of many colours to annoy other peacocks, nor does the lion grow its mane for spite. Coloured tails and flowing manes are Nature's way of expressing majesty; of setting a good impression. Pomp and power go together.

You have got to look a success before you are a success. If you have not got anything; if you have not got even a bean, you must somehow strive to look as though you owned the whole wide world, and you must dress the part.

The hero in that play, **The Man in Dress Clothes,** told the world to 'take everything, take my bed; **but leave me my dress clothes'.** He portrayed that a man could do without anything, even his bed, so long as he possessed the one important thing of all, a smart suit.

In everything, give a good impression. Nothing must be too good for you – the magician.

How about hats. Do you wear one? The really successful V.I.P. always wears a hat. Remember Macmillan, the Prime Minister, and how he startled a thousand Russians.

Oh, that wonderful, wonderful hat! Tall, white, furry, and distinguished, it did more for Anglo-Russian relations in ten minutes than diplomatic exchanges do in a month.

It hit the eye immediately Mr Macmillan stepped out of his Comet at Moscow Airport. It stopped a reception committee in its tracks. The people gasped with admiration.

Mr Kruschev smiled, gestured to the crowd, and said: **'They are saying what a beautiful hat you have.'**

It was not only the tallest among every conceivable variety of other hats. **It was the only white one.** On the head of the soldierly 6 ft Prime Minister, it set him apart and above everybody at the airport.

Where did Mr Macmillan get that hat? He bought it in Scandinavia. A Russian design. All white.

The late Shaw Desmond, the famous novelist, always wore a very beautiful emerald green silky fur hat, trilby style. It was indeed handsome against his white hair and he was very much admired wherever he went in it. Shaw Desmond was particularly successful. And, of course, the top hat. So splendid.

Hats express character. Remember Queen Mary's toque, Monty's beret with all the medallions on it, Maurice Chevalier's boater? They denote status, the Bishop's mitre, the Don's mortar board, the Ducal coronet. They convey moral qualities, the flamboyant hat of the Cavalier, the severely plain one of the Puritan. They promote political attitudes—Gandhi's forage cap.

You don't want to wear a hat, not even if it brings you magic? Then I suggest you send yourself a Get Well card. You are sick. You are never likely to work magic.

Gold is magical, make no mistake about it.

Women stepped out this summer in white sandals **glittering with gold**, and **gold** brings glittering success. For the winter boots have become the fashion, but never mind, there are glittering **gold** boots of Russian design, to wear with white. They do not cost the earth, as the **gold** doesn't have to be real.

People are having **gold** lampshades, **gold** chairs for their dining-rooms, **gold** plated plates, **golden** lustre casserole dishes, **gold** cups and saucers. I've seen glittering **gold** on a ceiling. All very wonderful. The Midas touch. It gives a luxurious impression.

When the famous Earl Blackwell emerges from his mid-Manhattan apartment every day and strides towards his office in Fifth Avenue, he is loaded with **gold**; a poem of splendour.

His trousers are held up by a **gold-tipped** Florentine belt. He wears solid **gold** cuff-links in his hand-made Italian shirt, and he extracts cigarettes from a **gold** case. The paper money in his pocket is held securely in a **gold** clip. He is elegant and immensely successful. If you want to make a note of something and ask to borrow his pen, he will hand you a ball-point with the name in **gold** letters embossed on it. All these **gold** treasures have been gifts. Good psychology. Speak to your subconscious and get a few **gold** presents yourself.

Anthony Steel, the film actor, wears a **gold** wrist chain, **gold** cuff-links, **gold** on his fingers. Gifts. There is something very magical about **gold**. It gives the right impression; the impression of wealth. You must concentrate on having **gold** about you and plenty in your environment. I have seen white velvet cushions with a **gold** monogram in the corner; white kid matchbox covers with a **gold** monogram on; white dressing-gowns with gold initials of the owner on the breast. Little touches that convey so much. **Gold** attracts **gold**.

Eddie Calvert, the man with the **Golden Trumpet**, and a **gold** recording disc, is very prosperous. When anyone talks of the man with a **gold** trumpet, you know it is Eddie Calvert. It is like a trade mark. The best of all trade marks.

Advertisers use **gold** to impress you. There is the **Golden Ring** products, **Golden Glory, Golden Lady,** and she wears a **golden** cape. There is the **Golden Arrow, The Golden Mile,** and that saying, 'the streets of London are paved with **gold**'. All to give a good impression; an impression of wealth.

So **do** get something **gold,** even if it is not real. The real will come later, when you are a fully fledged magician.

White always sets a good impression, too. **White** is for camellias, swansdown, moonlight – the good things. **White** spells luxury. Keep the house sparkling with clean **white** linen, bowls of **white** flowers, waxy **white** candles, and so on. The Queen Mother once thrilled and startled Paris in her **white** only wardrobe. **White** is the basic colour in the home of Douglas Fairbanks Jnr; white walls, white woodwork, white carpets. Most wealthy people surround themselves with the glamour of **white.** A very famous actor in summer walks about in an all-white beautifully tailored suit, with a **white** dog at his heels. It is the all-**white** house, the all-**white** caravan, a **white** car, that is the most glamorous and has the trade mark of success. Think this over, and act.

Impress with jewels. Take Barbara Cartland, the queen of romantic writers. To show you round the cowsheds at her magnificent five-acre farm in Hertfordshire, she will wear a full quota of beautiful jewellery; diamond bracelet, clip, and earrings. She hates slacks for women, and believes it does others good to see her like this – the cows and the cowmen! I take off my hat to her, she sets the most wonderful impression, and it does one good. Real jewels are something we should all possess.

If a man has not many suits, at least he can impress with waistcoats. Beau Brummell loved waistcoats, and one of his fashion whims was a jewelled waistcoat. He used velvet for his coats.

Velvet, of course, is another trade mark of success. A woman may look very nice in tweeds, but velvet makes her glamorous and lovely. Velvets and satins all come in the category of wealth; they impress you that way. A man in a velvet smoking-jacket at once looks prosperous. The nature of material can speak volumes, and if you are out to impress, consider this. I know a man can't walk about in a velvet or satin suit, but he can have a silk shirt, or a velvet or satin

128

dressing-gown. Embossed satin. Beverley Nichols has a glamorous dressing-gown which he often wears when he is writing. Do you run to hide when someone comes to the front door? Dressed to impress, you would welcome any visitor. And the visitor would think you prosperous. It is important that you impress people; your good luck depends so much upon what others think of you.

There was once a film called **Gone with the Wind** with a famous scene in which Scarlett O'Hara, the impoverished heroine, tried to fool the hero that she was a fine lady in velvet and pearls. She **almost** succeeded – her beauty and lovely clothes dazzled him. But when he went to kiss her hand, alas, her broken nails and rough, work-torn hands gave her away at once.

Moral of this tale: our hands often reveal much more about us than our face or clothes. Are you proud of your hands? Do pay attention to them; often as a mind-reader, a person's hands tell me a lot. Hand gestures when you speak can be very fascinating, like the French and other foreigners so often do, they can impress you. Make your hands tell a story; the story of your position and success.

You want to work magic. Play the part of a magician. It is an unnecessary disillusionment to see someone who claims to be able to work magic, buying cabbages or kippers, in a dingy mackintosh with bedraggled hair or a headscarf. Such a person looks about as glamorous as a housewife at the washing-machine or a man in the garden tending his manure heap.

You must be larger than life. You must be different from the man or woman next door. The inside of a crowded bus is not for you. Without becoming a hermit, you must live a shade apart. You must be an exotic personality. To be dowdy does not aid in the building up of a personality that is supposed to be a clever magician. You are expected to look different. You should set an example. You should make everyone else want to have a magic mind, like you have, and you

129

can only do that by playing the part. You have been learning. By the time you get to the end of this book you will have the full know-how. You will have **star** quality. You will have the aura of swimming pools, big cars, motor yachts, the lot. Give yourself the right background. Make the reaction terrific. Be head-and-shoulders above the common crowd. Be, oh, **so** demanding.

Are you vivid? Are you vital? I mean, if you would only pull yourself together and follow the advice in this book, you would be radiant, you would be prosperous. You would be a first-class magician.

There is the old amusing story of a man who was picked up unconscious from the gutter and taken into the house of a duke.

He was placed in the duke's bed, and treated in every way like a duke. When he regained consciousness, he protested against this, declaring that he was simply an ordinary man.

In spite of the most vehement protestations, however, those about him continued to treat him in every detail as a duke.

What happened? In the course of time, this man came to believe that he really **was** a duke, and that his idea of being an ordinary man must have been an hallucination.

No sooner had he come to this conclusion than he began to put on noble airs. He even spoke with a princely accent. No longer did he have the characteristics of a down-and-out from the gutter, but walked the world like a nobleman.

It can be the same with you. You think you are an ordinary person. If you were you would never have bought this book. But something inside you **knew** you were a magician, and that 'something' urged you to study magic. Once you realize you **are** a magician, you will realize that the idea of yourself being just an ordinary man was an hallucination. You will begin to talk **positive**, like a magician. You will begin to **act** like a magician, you will walk with your head high and **know** that you – of all people – **can work magic**.

A gentleman staying at the Dorchester was offering a fine

job with big money to the kind of person he wanted. A certain man who wanted the job did not answer his advertisement, but borrowed money and clothes, and went to stay at the Dorchester himself. Like that he would meet the man and they would get talking, and he would get the job. **He did.** That man had brought out the magic in his mind when he decided to be on the spot, and it worked.

Another man after a big job with big money attached to it, bluffed his way into the position. The job was for someone who was in a position to entertain lavishly. This man asked a friend of his who had a lovely home and servants, to loan him his house and servants for that one particular appointment. When the 'boss' arrived to see what possibility there was of the man being able to carry out his wishes, he saw the lovely home and servants, and engaged him there and then! If your environment is not right, stay at a big hotel or borrow some friend's home, anything, any trick, that will bring you magic. At all costs, set a good impression.

You wonder. How about **me**? I have my **velvet** jacket, many have seen me wearing it on television sometimes. Amongst my **golden** treasures is the **gold-tipped** cigarette-holder I use. But perhaps my greatest treasure of all is the **gold** medal of the Magicians' Club, which I won at the age of sixteen – the youngest ever. That little bit of **gold** means a lot to me. Here is an extract from **Television Mirror, May 29th, 1954.**

'Al Koran tells me that tonight he is going to attempt something never before done on television.

"No predictions. No racing forecasts," Al said. Pressed for further details, he added, "You can call it applied psychology."

I hereby call it that, and add that for his next TV spot in June, Al Koran will try something even bigger, involving, in my guess, a transatlantic hook-up in psychology.

As the comic conjurer used to tell his audience, "My next trick is impossible." '

And then, from **Edinburgh Pictorial, August 6th, 1954.**

'Whether you believe in mind-reading or not, you would find Al Koran uncanny. This young man . . . accomplishes the seemingly impossible – swiftly and accurately.'
Mark Johns in the Daily Sketch.

'I salute him.'

12
The Magic Of Laughter

'IF you want to **attract** people,' said the late Sir Thomas Lipton, **'make them laugh.'** His own big company, operating hundreds of retail shops, had two big mirrors in every shop – one concave and one convex. What happened? The people going in saw themselves long, thin, and hungry-looking. When they came out the mirror showed them short, fat, happy – **laughing.**

Now this was wonderful psychology. Hundreds of people would go to the shops, buy, and roar with laughter as they came out. It was a clever idea, a bit mad perhaps, but a good sales stunt. He attracted people by **making them laugh.** You can do it every time.

When Ella Wheeler Wilcox wrote **Laugh and the world laughs with you,** take it from me, she knew what she was saying.

People want to laugh, only they are afraid to let their hair down. Have you ever smiled to somebody across the hotel lounge? Somebody you don't know. I guess you haven't. You've grown too far in on yourself. You are in danger of never getting out. You have forgotten what it's like to behave in a free way. Throw off that tight, restricting feeling which stops you tasting some of the fun of being alive. I was larking about the other night, and someone said, 'Do you know, we haven't had such fun as this since the war.' Isn't that just the saddest thing you ever heard?

In this country it rains a lot. You grumble. You become irritable. Why? Some of the happiest times of my life have been spent in the rain; **laughing in the rain.** Children do not run away from rain, they paddle in the puddles and laugh. Like a little boy I know, when it was raining hard beating a tattoo on the caravan roof, he sneaked out of bed in the early morning in his pyjamas, and scampered about the wet grass. His father, missing him, discovered what he was up to and said, 'You naughty boy coming out in your pyjamas like this when it's raining.' The little boy looked at him with a smile and said, 'Well, I've got me 'at on!' They both laughed.

I have heard people coming from a show saying, 'Oh, I feel ever so much better for that laugh!' And it is true, they **do** feel better.

Laughter is a stimulant. Consistent cheeriness helps us to keep our chins up, it counter-balances the trying times.

What is it that keeps the soldier going, although so often he is in the midst of bloodshed? What is it that keeps the sailor from losing his nerve? It is **laughter**; the cheerful companionship of his pals. They see the funny side of things.

I am sure you know the kind of laughter I mean. It is a hearty, merry, generous sound; love and no more hating; laughter vital enough to move the most bitter man or woman.

When I do magic on the stage or television, I don't pull a long face. I smile. I laugh. I am happy. It is a necessary part of magic – this laughter. That itself puts you on a higher plane; helps to make you very magnetic.

One of the finest personalities we have today, beloved for his wonderful sense of humour, is the Duke of Edinburgh. At an Edinburgh banquet he used Shaw's naughty adjective from **Pygmalion.** Members of the Royal College of Surgeons had presented him with a silver bleeding cup to commemorate his visit.

Fellows of the college howled with mirth when the president, Mr Walter Mercer, ended his speech: 'May it please your Royal Highness to accept this bleeding cup.'

There were great gusts of laughter as the Duke took the cup and said: **'I can only say it is bloody kind of you.'**

The world today needs laughter, and how well the Duke of Edinburgh knows this. You can always be sure of a good laugh when he is around.

Magic and gaiety go together. Where you have one you have the other. When you work magic for yourself, you are gay. When you are gay, **you work magic.** The two go hand in hand.

A little boy made me laugh the other day. He had been taught to say the Lord's Prayer, so my friend encouraged him to go on from there and pray for his parents.

So the small boy said: 'Please God look after Mummie and Daddy and Uncle Peter . . . and please God look after yourself, because if anything happens to you, we're all sunk!'

During a sale in a department store the other day, I saw a young woman shopping with difficulty. The small daughter at her side tugged and pulled at her mother's skirt.

Suddenly the distressed woman said softly: **'Quick, Mary, just be calm now and take it easy.'**

The assistant congratulated her on her psychology. Then smiling at the child, he said: 'So your name is Mary?'

'Oh no,' said the mother. 'Her name is Jill – I'm Mary.'

Then they both broke into hearty laughter.

She was a real psychologist, that woman, using her affirmations at the right time.

Remember Yuri Gagarin who first conquered space? Everyone fell for him. Yuri has that gallant way of concentrating on **you** when he is with you, not peeping round for someone more important. But it was his charming smile that got everyone. Lady Hailsham loved it, and the women who saw it went overboard for him.

135

Noel Coward has a wonderful sense of humour. He once sent a wire to some people with whom he was going to stay in the country. To make certain the strangers who were to meet him at the station would know him, he wired. **Shall arrive by the 12.30 train looking extremely handsome in pale grey.**

How they must have laughed.

Laughter is a right and a duty. The magic of laughter cures all human despair. It brings out the magic in your mind, and in the minds of other people.

'I don't care a damn.' This was engraved on the little image of Buddha which Gabriele D'Annunzio always carried on his person. When his superiors annoyed him and he was forbidden by discipline to make a reply, he would silently exhibit the Buddha, and give a little laugh.

The thought 'I don't care a damn' was engraved on D'Annunzio's heart as well as his mascot. If you read all about Europe's most picturesque figure, you will be filled with admiration at the laughing spirit of this splendid man.

When somebody wrote, 'I don't care for the Big Bad Wolf' that somebody made a fortune! Because it was a sound, laughing philosophy, and people liked it; felt better when they sang it.

It is said that Charles the First, awaiting the fatal day which was to end his life, asked to have some kittens in his room that he might laugh at their gambols. A sense of humour helps us to be brave, better sports to 'take it on the chin'.

Every day you meet a certain number of people, some with long faces, others with a smile that won't come off.

You may be sitting in the bus or railway carriage as they pass. You may, perhaps, never see those people again.

There are some who always wear the expression of a graven image, they smile not, neither do they grin.

You never give them a second thought.

But during the day, even if you are ever so busy, you often recall for a moment a face that smiled at you.

I have often wondered why some people fascinate me, and in every case it has been the smile or the laughter, that made the strongest appeal.

The sudden uplifting of the corners of a mouth, the beautiful curve of a cheek, the revealing of nice teeth, and then the gradual fading of that smile; the indescribable something which lingers a little while after the smile has gone, like the afterglow of a sunset.

That is how I would describe all the smiles that have charmed me.

There are the big smiles, belonging to a generously pro-portioned mouth, the baby smiles belonging to small pouting mouths, the shy smiles, the sad smiles, the mischievous smiles.

Are your smiles the winning or losing kind? The winning kind attract, and bring magic into your life. One feels instinctively that a lovely smile reveals a lovely soul. It is the outward sign of an inward invisible beauty. It is something which remains in your memory long after the eyes, even, are forgotten.

No one has the strength to stand up against a beautiful smile, or a hearty laugh. No one can resist them. The magic is powerful and infectious.

Many people smile with their mouths only, while their eyes remain quite expressionless. These are mechanical smiles of the salad-without-dressing variety. They are empty, nothing comes from such a smile. They mean less than nothing.

Laughter makes the world go round. Smiles keep the old young, the young healthy, increase the girth of the lean, give to the stout that enviable reputation for good fellowship, keep the doctor away, colour the drab with splashes of gold and silver, reduce the haughty, elevate the humble, break down the silly barriers of class distinction and level humanity, show all things in their true perspective, and **work magic**.

Laugh your problems away is the motto of Dr Murray Banks, the New York psychiatrist and lecturer turned entertainer.

'Laughter releases us from the restraints, inhibitions, and strain of modern living,' he says. 'If you can laugh, you are mentally healthy; the mentally ill can't laugh.'

He gave up being a doctor to go on the stage and make people laugh.

This doctor realizes the great value to health that laughter really is.

Laughing gives you a zest for living, and helps you to live to a very old age. London public health chiefs, recently probing the statistics of deaths from coronary thrombosis and other diseases, found increasing evidence that it was the man or woman who refused to worry about keeping up with the Joneses, and laughed, that escaped these illnesses.

'I am sure of this myself,' said a borough medical officer of health. 'The man or woman **who can laugh** and does not give a hoot for anything, gets a kick out of life and lives longer.'

This is supported by public health experts in many other parts of the country, some of whom have been so impressed by their findings, that they have reported them to their councils.

Dr Hector Mackenzie-Wintle, a medical officer in charge of the South Oxfordshire combined districts, urges us to **stop worrying, and laugh.** He believes that laughter keeps us fit. I agree. I know it to be true.

Ken Roberts, the effervescent comedian, who fills the theatre wherever he appears, knows how to project side-splitting laughter from the moment he comes before the footlights.

What makes him so effervescent? **Laughter.** 'Life was given us to enjoy,' he says. 'The secret for me is this – that happiness is a thing called **now.** I feel so strongly about it, that I pass it on to others. There is youthful magic in laughter.'

Laughter is positive. Laugh, and you keep a clean, healthy mind. The body reacts at once. Carrying a grudge against people and things is disastrous to health. Most people would like their family doctor to live next door to them, so that they

138

could keep calling on him. Laughter can prevent you needing any doctor. The magic of it wins over all your setbacks, enables you to triumph over wrongs, and banishes all fears. You need never dread a nervous breakdown if you laugh.

How does Ken keep so fit; all those exhausting rehearsals, all that scriptwriting, all that travel, travel, travel? 'I just laugh and feel happy about it,' he says. 'Laughter lifts any exhaustion; I feel light and gay.'

Don't you feel lifted up when you laugh?

So many people today look sad, tired out, and overworked. Yet the fact remains that their laughter can be induced by a comedian, which is proof their ability to laugh has not died, as some would think. Millions of people are alive today who are not truly living. They are alive because their hearts go on beating. But they are tired, and they are sick. They get no sheer, exhilarating joy out of being alive. They deny themselves real fun. They do not laugh enough. Good fooling is good medicine. Health must be made every day – that's the point to remember. You should laugh every day, morning, noon, and night.

What made Sinbad so rich? You will remember how he related the story of his seven voyages to a poor, discontented porter named Hinbad in order to show him that wealth must be obtained by personal exertion. I like particularly the story of his fifth voyage when, swimming to a desert island after his ship had been dashed to pieces, he threw stones at the monkeys so that they should throw back coco-nuts to him. This was something more than enterprise in adversity; it was a sense of humour which was Sinbad's salvation in his darkest hour. It made him laugh so heartily, it helped him to amass the riches to which he was so justly entitled at the end of the perilous voyage. Laughter saved him, and it was laughter that attracted the riches.

It is easy to talk with a smile. You can convey any message by the way you look, smile, or laugh? It is the most international language of all. Without any words, you can use hand gestures and a smile, and make yourself understood. But without the smile you are completely stuck. Nobody will take notice of you; nobody will be attracted.

In a past chapter I suggested that you carry in your pocket a playing card, the King or Queen of Hearts. I now suggest in all earnestness that you slip into your pocket or handbag the **Jester**, as a constant reminder to you, to laugh.

[It is not work that breaks you down. Neither is it the problems that you have to solve. It is the wrong attitude of mind.]And when you are determined not to smile or laugh, you have the wrong attitude. If you are never going to laugh at your troubles, then you need read no farther.

How often do you go to a musical comedy or variety show? There is always a good comedian, paid big money to make you laugh. It is much easier to move people to tears than to win them over to laughter. But they do it.

What sort of men are they off-stage? They are among the most serious of men. Those who remember the late George Robey will remember that he was the creator of beautiful music, making violins and a lover of beautiful china, of which he had a marvellous collection. To know him was to add to one's education in artistry. Charlie Chaplin has a tremendous interest in vegetarianism; Danny Kaye does untold good work for millions of children all over the world. I could go on naming an endless number of them, all deeply thoughtful. These men who make us laugh are all real Thinkers. The more you laugh, the more you raise yourself up to that plane where magic comes. Comedians work magic through sheer laughter. They never lack friends.

If you want magic in your life, you must smile, you must laugh. Use this tremendous pivot power that makes you a force that can hold sway, destruct, or construct. It is said that anybody can play the fool well. But you, who know why you are laughing (because I have been telling you) know that it brings the magic out of your mind. Magical things will happen all around you. Play the fool well. Laughter comes

140

before all. For lack of it many a man goes down, and stays down.

Thousands of people are going down because they cannot bring themselves to laugh. To be out of touch with the young, is to be out of touch with laughter. Today the world is for the young. You must mix with them. To be out of touch with young people is to be out of touch with laughter and magic.

Why deny yourself healthy fun and exhilarating joy? Why be crabby, miserable, and complaining? It doesn't get you anywhere. But laughter does. Laughter gets you health and wealth and attracts the things you want in life.

Mix with people who laugh, and go to the theatre where a comedian tops the bill. Write and tell them how they made you laugh. Get a laughing signed photograph and keep it somewhere prominent, to remind you of what I am saying; to inspire you to do the same. Go back-stage and meet the comedians and laugh together all over again. Touch their lives with your own, share their fun, their hopes, their dreams. Invite them to your home, take them for a drive out into the country in your car. Drink with them. **Do not cut yourself off from the magic of laughter,** but go all out to experience the thrill that comes when you share laughter, if only for a moment.

How much are you a part of other laughing lives? You must strive to be, for laughter is catching.

Did you see the Royal Variety Performance at the theatre or on television? The show where the wonderful and ageless **Maurice Chevalier** appeared. The radiant Queen Mother will always remember his smile, and the charming way he looked up at her as she sat, so glamorous, glittering with diamonds, in the Box. She is never likely to forget the endearing way he smiled and sang, **'You must have been a beautiful baby – 'cos baby look at you now.'** Her sweet smile of appreciation captured all hearts. Those were the two loveliest smiles one is ever likely to see.

141

It was Sterne who said: 'Every time a man smiles, much more when he laughs, it adds something to his fragment of life.'

And that 'something' is – **magic**.

Do I make people laugh?

Here is an extract from the Times of Malta:

'. . . Koran gave a miniature preview to the Press at the Hotel Astra last night. "This is only a side-line," he explained as he took out a pack of playing cards. Three men each took a card. There was no possibility of Koran seeing the cards. And yet he knew what suit and denomination they were.

Another demonstration of mind-reading was given when he asked a Press representative to think of any number between 1 and 99, and write it on a piece of paper, out of sight of Koran and the bystanders. In a few seconds Koran knew the number. It was 17.'

These things made them laugh. They couldn't understand it. They were spellbound. All they could do was laugh, and congratulate me.

13
The Magic Of Colour

THERE are many things you come up against in your daily life that are necessary to you, if you would work magic. I have told you about the flowers, and perhaps you have never thought of them that way before, and colour is another thing that is of vital importance.

Let us first consider colour, and how it radiates an aura around each individual. It is invisible to the eye unless you are clairvoyant. The aura extends in a radius of about four feet, though a very enlightened soul may have an aura several yards in diameter. All colours seen in the auric centre possess a definite interpretation, and those who have studied this sort of thing can give one look at you and reveal many truths.

By loving everybody you develop the **rose-pink** colour of loving kindness in your aura. And this colour attracts, whereas dull colours are negative and can only attract ill-health and harm. You link yourself with others who have this dullness in their aura and you take on their ills and worries, then wonder why you are not feeling so bright.

By doing and thinking only those things which will give your aura that **rose-pink** glow, you are protecting yourself against all that is bad. To make sure that nothing and nobody can penetrate this condition, cross one foot over the other, and close your hands. Your centre is then closed and nothing can disturb you until you unloose yourself. But you must be on your guard, immediately 'cutting off' when necessary. I would like you to remember this; it is so easy to do, yet so valuable. The more clear, clean, and beautiful you can make your aura, the more you can work magic.

Colour must be one of the first needs in your life. If you are feeling fed up and depressed, that means that you are simply surrounding yourself with the wrong colours. How colourful is your world? Have you ever thought about it? Don't accept drabness. When colour enlivens your environment, depression drifts away. When you are bored you cut yourself off from that power which works magic, so determine to capture the tonic effect of colour.

Colour has a great effect upon you, for good or bad. It can have an effect upon you in the decoration of your home, in the things you use every day; the colour of your car, your pen, your motor yacht, your suit, indeed everything you possess. It can affect your whole outlook on life. You vibrate to a particular Ray and express the characteristic of that Ray.

Babies react to vivid colours, and the reaction expands as we grow up. An experiment was recently carried out where small children were put in a grey-walled room, and others in a yellow room. The 'yellows' were completely free of illness, but the 'greys' were coughing and sneezing and generally run down.

There is a super-hospital at Munich, in which every room is a different colour. It was here where they took the survivors of the Manchester United football team after the terrible air crash. I think this idea of every room being a different colour is splendid and sane, because colour can make all the difference between life and death, as this hospital realized.

The study where you go to meditate should have walls decorated in your favourite colour. You can have it in violet if you like, which is the lightest and best vibration-colour.

144

In 1947, British Airways noticed that many of their passengers suffered from air-sickness. The plane was decorated in yellow. They changed it to sky-blue and there was a very marked improvement at once.

To go back to the aura, there is a wonderful sea of colour around each individual and when you have learnt how to magnetize conditions, then you discover the secret of demonstration. You are attracted to that which you are in tune with. The colour you wear attracts or repels.

Your body needs sunlight which gives you ultra-violet and infra-red treatment. To obtain sunlight one does not have to see the sun actually shining. The sun is shining on a rainy day, as you would see if you went high up in an aeroplane. The body needs colour as well as sunshine, and there is no excuse these days for not having plenty of colour around you. If you do not look after your body and give it what it wants, how can you ever expect to work magic? You must be healthy, and you must pay attention to colour. You must have an awareness. You must be aware of the power of radiation.

We so often make our climate the scapegoat for dull and drab colour schemes. A French artist once called the English colour-blind. The Italians use under-water colours; violet, sapphire, turquoise, aqua-marine, coral, ice-cream pink, and yellow. They put pink against scarlet, red against orange, and colours we would not dream of putting together. Have you ever studied the colours in the shop windows from Milan to Rome? They specialize in one-colour displays, and it makes you feel very eager to have that one particular colour, because it is so vital and attractive. The punch of these under-water colours impels you to buy. They are marvellous. What the Italians do with colour is an education. It was Ruskin who said: 'The purest and most thoughtful minds are those which love colour the most.'

A man who directs racing on television programmes told me he is still surprised by one thing in his job. He spends a long time cooped up in the control panel of the scanner-van directing the cameras.

'But every time I come out I am amazed at the lovely colours of a racecourse,' he said. 'The green grass, white rails and stands, the colour of the horses and the jockey's racing silks. It is a wonderful spectacle. One day it will make beautiful colour television.'

Do you notice colours when you are out? You should, and you should go where colour predominates, like parks with beautiful coloured flowers, art galleries, look in jewellers' shop windows, greyhound racing (their little coloured jackets racing by), the kilts of Bonnie Scotland, or the spectacle of a musical show. Here you see lavish colour which takes your breath away, and is exciting just to look at. People go to musical shows to get out of themselves; to get away from the monotony and dreariness of everyday routine. The beauty of coloured dresses in movement, such as one sees when dancers spin in a blaze of coloured light, produces an exhilarating effect upon an audience which is unique and exotic – a feast for the eyes. In the hands of an imaginative producer, the theatre can give us colour and spectacle that can do us a power of good. Are you seeing enough colour?

One of the most pathetic spectacles is the man or woman whose mind is closed to the beauty and romance of colour. Everyone who strives for more and more colour lives more happily, because besides one's real life, one also lives a fairy-tale life. I recall the yards and yards of coloured tulle worn on the petticoats worn by dancers beneath gorgeous bouffant skirts. It all looks so frothy and enchanting as they float over the stage, see what I mean? Colour makes you a little more real, a little more lovely, and a little more dear to everyone you meet. That's magic.

Do you wear coloured shoes? Have you a coloured umbrella, pair of gloves, or a coloured mackintosh? Do you cook in coloured saucepans, drink from coloured glasses, wash with a coloured sponge, and dry yourself with a coloured towel? Do you sleep in coloured sheets? Are your nightclothes bright, and your slippers gay? Is your car and your travelling case a colour that cheers? There are thousands of people wanting to be a mental magician, but few of them turn to colour. Your day should be full of fascinating colours, your favourite colour predominating. Have you seen the sun shining through coloured glass ornaments? It is beautiful. Coloured glass attracts the light with a brilliance undreamed of, and these colours help to bring magic into your life.

And you should visualize colours. Get small pieces of silks or satins of very vivid colours and some of pastel shades. Clip them together. Concentrate on certain colours; look at them, think of them, draw power from them. Look at **violet** or **amethyst** if you want to reach a higher dimension, to purify your mind or solve a problem.

If its money and abundance you want, concentrate on the little square of **emerald green** silk.

To sharpen your intellect, **yellow** is helpful.

Look at these little pieces of coloured silk daily until you become completely colour-conscious; until you feel within you the urge to have plenty of colour in your environment, and on your body. Until you become **aware** of the value of colour.

Can the colours you wear affect you? It can, one colour can bring a person luck, whilst the same colour can be harmful to another. It depends on your particular Ray.

'The wearing of **emerald green** has always brought me immense good luck,' said a lady author. But **scarlet** brings me bad luck, like the time I was wearing a **scarlet** dress, and broke my arm. This lady wrote a book which was rejected by the publishers. But she sent it back immediately, in an **emerald green** cover, and it was accepted. Don't ask me to explain it. **Emerald green** is that particular lady's magic colour, and **you** have colours that are magic, too.

John Slater, the famous stage and television actor, says, 'When it comes to television, you won't find me wearing **green** again.'

Then he goes on, 'It wasn't easy getting into television. I tried over and over again, but misfortune pursued me. Time and time again I missed my chance of appearing on the screen through bad luck.'

He continues: 'Then one day it dawned on me. I came to realize that all the things I had worn at Lime Grove were **green; green** tie, **green** pullover, **green** socks. So I decided to try another colour.

I went to see the producer again, with not even the tiniest spot of **green** anywhere. What happened? **My luck changed immediately!**

I realize that colour **can** influence one's life; how could I believe otherwise?'

Barbara Cartland, with many romantic novels to her credit, says, '**Green** is very lucky for me.'

Colour means nothing to some people; the sort of people who don't like animals, flowers, music, or the laughter of little children. But colour is magic, and can influence your life. And the marvellous power of colour vibration can dissolve many of our ills. Just as the ancients recognized colour as a master science, so can we study it and turn to it as a cure. It is a proven fact that by the right use of colour we can rebuild our body.

Do you suffer from neurosis, a result of this age of speedy living? You can find new health through the stimulating and soothing effect of colour prescription.

Your world should be full of colour, the particular shades essential to your health and happiness. It is impossible to be happy, continually optimistic, and possess a positive mind, if you surround yourself with depressing, mournful colours. The atmosphere of the world, and your own well-being, can be changed from the lower dimension to the higher, by the right use of colour.

Melancholia and acute depression have been completely cured by synchronized colour. At the Chicago State Hospital for the Insane, an apparatus called colorama has been used which throws upon the screen abstract patterns of rainbow colours, constantly melting into one colour. This appeal to the eye has proved most wonderfully beneficial to the patients. Many modern cinemas show a similar colour screen prior to the pictures. It bathes, relaxes, and refreshes the tired mind.

Pure **blood red** is used quite frequently for healing. It is very good for the circulation of the blood and restores vitality. If you are feeling 'fed up' and want your vitality restored, put on **scarlet** slippers, or place a bowl of **scarlet** flowers somewhere prominent. The magic will come. You will soon begin to feel alive again.

There was the case of the doctor who believed in the power of colour to heal, and he used it on a boy of eight years who was almost totally paralysed. He robed the boy in **white**, and then used strong light baths. At the end of three weeks the child could walk. Colour has a positive therapeutic value, and if used freely enough, can cure dyspepsia. By wearing **red** garments the colour has actually been proved to seep into the skin and make a man strong and dynamic.

Raymond Twyeffort, the famous New York tailor, developed acute stomach trouble, but doctors could find nothing wrong. Then one day he put on a **scarlet** hunting coat, and felt so exhilarated that he began to wear vibrant ties, socks, pyjamas, shirts, and dressing-gowns. **His stomach troubles vanished.** Colour, that works magic, had cured him.

Scarlet cloth, particularly flannel, is highly recommended for lumbago and all cases of rheumatism. All sufferers from this distressing complaint should try the magic of **scarlet** flannel, the brightest possible colour. Once you have proof all your own, nothing can shake your conviction. But you have never given it a thought, perhaps, never believed that there is magic in colour.

Those who suffer from sleeplessness should try sleeping in a blue room. If the walls are the wrong shade, try flooding the room with blue lights. **Turquoise blue** is the most helpful colour if you suffer from headaches.

Green is employed for the decoration of eye hospitals, because **green** is most helpful to the sight.

Yellow is invigorating and acts on the nerves and brain. If you have a worrying problem, this colour will help you.

Violet is electrical and can be used as a tonic. The higher the vibration the more powerful it is. **Violet** is a powerful colour. X-rays, which are above the **violet**, enable us to 'see through things'.

All extremely nervous people will benefit if they wear the colour **amethyst.** Also let them live in rooms where **purple, mauve,** or **heliotrope** are the chief colours, and choose their clothes of the same shade. In all the most modern mental institutions **mauve** or **heliotrope** is the colour used for the decoration of the rooms in which acutely nervous cases are treated, since those colours are the most soothing and healing to the mind. Shades ranging from **violet** to **purple** are excellent in cases of hysteria.

Nature emphasizes the importance of colour, and it is best to live as near to nature as you can. Imagine a world without the **green** of the fields, the **blue** of the skies, the **red** breast of a robin, the **gold** of the coach of a King!

You should see as much colour as you can; the beautiful Taj Mahal, inlaid with precious stones, jewels of marvellous colours that change their tints with the setting sun. And I think of one of the smallest pictures in the Tate Gallery, which shows such exquisite colours that it attracts more attention than any other picture, and tremendous sums of money have been offered for it. 'The Death of Chatterton' has to be seen to be believed, it is indescribably lovely; the young poet's magnificent flaming **red** hair, the **blue** of his breeches so unlike any other **blue**; why, nobody could gaze at such a picture without being deeply moved by its colour.

What would the children do if Santa Claus was not dressed in **red**?

Confront any man with a row of pretty girls. Put each in different coloured dresses, and ask him which looks the prettiest. I'm a mind-reader, and I know. He'll say, 'Who's that girl in blue. . . .?' It is psychology. Blue is a winner with men. She adores forget-me-nots, bluebells, blue hyacinths, blue flowers of every kind. Do you feel nostalgic when you hear the music Blue Skies? Of course you do. Blue has a magic all its own. As a magician I have many times drawn coloured silk handkerchiefs out of a tube container. There is nothing to it, but the audience applaud. They love the colours. All magicians use colour in their performances. Magic and colour go together.

You should have plenty of colour in your diet. The most colourful food is the most nourishing. Glowing red tomatoes, yellow melons and grapefruit, green and red apples, deep blue grapes, red cherries, pink shrimps, and so on. There are thousands of people longing to make the greatest success of their lives, yet few of them turn to colour.

You should start the day with plenty of colour. An English breakfast, particularly now women go out to work, is usually the most neglected meal of the day. It is a rushed affair, with no thought to colour – 'Oh, breakfast doesn't matter, it can be served anyhow.'

This is fatal. You should give consideration to the first meal of the day; not only to what you are going to eat, but how it is laid out. Is there any colour; a coloured cloth or flowers on the table? Are the cups and saucers and plates a pretty colour? The colours you begin the day with will determine the pleasure and prosperity you will get out of it. So begin with plenty of colour.

Do you open your eyes to colour, in the bedroom? Colour simply must be introduced the moment you wake up. Don't you realize that? Have you never given it a thought?

When we were very young we were attracted to coloured toys; a yellow teddy bear, a red train, a blue motor car. Colour is the one thing that little ones really notice. A child faddy about drinking anything will often drink from a coloured pitcher and like it. A child who won't eat eggs often enjoys

151

it if the shell is painted a pretty colour. A mother whose baby son would not eat rice pudding, made it **pink** one day with a touch of cochineal, and the child cleaned his plate and **asked for more!** This is perfectly true. All children respond to colour. So do **you**, only you refuse to realize it.

Colour has its source in light, and in the beginning the Great Psychologist said, **Let there be Light.** In other words – **Let there be Colour.**

You vibrate in response to colour and you have to learn to tune-in to the dominant colour that you respond to upon your own particular Ray. You must place colour as one of the first needs in your life, because of its magic power. You must use colour in your diet, if you want to be healthy, see it in your home, in your clothes, and in every phase of your life. You must have **colour awareness.** All you need to recapture the exciting effect that colour had for you as a child, is a rekindling of interest in it. Make your world a colourful place to live in and you will be exuberant, vibrant, a live scintillating being.

Goethe said: 'Every individual colour makes on men an impression of its own, and thereby reveals its nature to the eye as well as to the mind.' This, of course, is right.

Christmas, when people are at their happiest and best, is always a riot of colour. The party dresses, the paper hats, the balloons, crackers, garlands, gifts and cards. Coloured lights on the Christmas tree, bright toys, flowers of every hue, everything gay with plenty of colour. There is goodwill towards all, not only because it is a religious festival, but because of the magic that colour brings.

Colour plays a real part in some of my performances. Some of you have seen me on stage, handing a stranger a long narrow box, in which is placed six coloured balls.

I stand with my back to the stranger and close my eyes. Then I ask him to choose which ball he fancies and put it in his right-hand jacket pocket. Now choose another and put it in the left-hand pocket, and so on.

Then I turn and face the stranger. 'In your right-hand pocket you have a red ball.' He draws it out and holds it up for the audience to see. Correct. 'In your left-hand pocket you have a green ball.' He draws it out of his pocket, and I am right again. I tell him the colour of the ball which he has left in the box, although I cannot see it. And I am correct again.

I have never been wrong. I like working with colours, and I always know the colour a person has chosen.

14
The Magic Of Flowers

'If you have two loaves of bread, sell one and buy a lily.' This is an old Chinese proverb, and the Chinese had something there. But the proverb could apply to any flower, even those of the wild variety. They can do so much to bring out the magic in your mind. It was flowers which outshone the glory of Solomon!

You should always have flowers in your home or office, real flowers and not the artificial ones so popular today, even though they are very realistic. And you should have them in the room where you meditate.

Flowers help to raise the mind and have great healing properties. Flowers raise the act of meditation to the highest levels, to one of real usefulness in helping you to make headway spiritually and materially. They are positive; they are productive of meritorious thought. At the time of arranging them in your home or 'retreat', you may reflect that this has been the practice of the Tibetans, and the saintly. You may reflect on the flower's perfection, and the more often you do this, the more often will that flower help to rule out greed, hatred, anger that leads to tears, and ignorance which makes this life of yours what it is, a state of anxiety and unhappiness most of the while.

A flower is Beauty itself. You see that it is a lovely colour, that it emanates sweet scent, and that it is soft to the touch. It influences you to be gentle. Surround yourself with flowers **and watch the results.** Flowers are vibratory, and give off radiations of a positive kind.

In the old days, men used to wear flowers in their button-holes. And if you have seen them, you will have observed that it was always the smiling, happy men, who wore them. The happier they were, the bigger the buttonhole. It was as though the flowers had a wonderful effect upon them. Today you only seem to see men with a buttonhole at weddings, or on some especially gay occasion. And much of the laughter has gone.

I have known women replace a pearl necklace with real gardenias on the neck, supported by transparent adhesive tape. It is far more glamorous than the most costly pearls. I have seen real flowers worn as earrings.

A blue-eyed beauty with flowers in her hair once caused a traffic-block. An artist saw her, and he was carried away with her loveliness. She became a famous model. 'It was the flowers in her hair that got me,' he said. 'I wish more English girls wore them.' And I learned that every morning the florist at her bus-stop had fresh flowers ready for her to pin in her hair. She attracted admirers wherever she went, because of this romantic touch. And through those flowers she became famous. Through flowers a state of happiness can be achieved beyond the power of most of us to understand.

When people you know suddenly ignore you, or when they try to pick a quarrel, don't tell them off or send a nasty letter. **Send flowers.** Flowers bring harmony and peace. They have a power all their own, and you can **say it with flowers.**

Do you know the language of flowers?

As soon as man was sufficiently civilized to have any appreciation of the aesthetic, he became vividly aware of the beauty of Nature's blossoms. There followed a symbolic and mystic attribution to these qualities and meanings. Beautiful and poetic thoughts were conveyed by the presentation of a sprig of blossoms, and whole messages were communicated by bouquets in which each flower chosen betokened a significant idea. Not only love and happiness were the tenor of these floral missives; coquetry, dalliance, indifference, and coolness; rebuff, refusal, scorn, contempt – all were expressed by a suitably chosen flower.

It is worth remembering that flowers can be 'telegraphed' to many parts of the world. Oceans and continents present no barriers to the floral message, which can bring out the magic in the mind of the one you send them to.

Here are some examples:

Forget-Me-Not – speaks for itself.

Red Rose – 'I love you.'

White Rose – 'I love you not.'

Red Carnation – Passionate love. 'I must see you soon.'

Bronze Chrysanthemum – Friendship. 'Though I value your friendship, I cannot love you.'

Tiger Lily – Passion. 'My love knows no bounds.'

Mistletoe – 'I send you a thousand kisses.'

The ancients used this way of speaking to each other, and for those who are shy, it can be very useful. You will reap endless joy in giving flowers which have a meaning. It is good psychology, and there is magic in it both for him who gives and the one who receives. When you give thought to flowers, what they mean and what they can do for you, you are on the right lines for happiness and success.

Many famous personalities have made use of flowers to express their feelings. Nero, who was fond of extravagant displays, enhanced the glory of one of his entertainments by covering the whole surface of Lake Lucila with roses. What a wonderful sight it must have been. Cleopatra, for one of her feasts she gave to honour Antony, caused the floor of her palace to be covered to a depth of eighteen inches with sweet-smelling rose petals. There's romance for you.

Stories of the rose are innumerable; so innumerable that

H. L. V. Fletcher, novelist, horticultural writer and rosarian, has distilled the 'attar' of a lifetime's love for all to enjoy and treasure and read again in his magnificent book, **The Rose Anthology.**

It has been said of this remarkable anthology of prose and verse set in a framework of Fletcher's personal comment that it offers something for every rose-lover. But surely, they must mean everyone, for the Rose is the flower of all the world; it has been revered throughout the ages, and should constantly remind us of a glory which cannot be matched by man.

If you would be reminded of this glory, then, I would commend the book's pride of place in the room which I have already suggested you should try to set aside for your meditation. You will be bound to gain much from it, and you will be glad, as I am, that Fletcher did not fail to include within its many enchanting pages what is, perhaps, the finest and most moving story of all – The Rose of Life. You know it? In case not, let me tell you briefly. Surgeons carrying out the most intricate of operations on the heart, pin a single red rose of life on the machine that takes over the functions of heart and lungs, while they sew up a tear in the heart itself.

The rose remains within sight of the waking patient, to whom it will be presented by the theatre sister. At one famous hospital, no heart operation begins until the rose ritual has been completed.

This is magic psychology. Think what it must mean to the waking patient to encounter such beauty. You should always keep one **Rose of Life in a single vase.**

Harry Wheatcroft, probably the most celebrated rose-grower alive, says, 'He who would grow good roses must have roses in his heart.' And he is a pacifist. 'I deplore beyond all measure the thousands of millions spent to create implements to destroy mankind. With all that money everybody could grow roses. The world could be made so beautiful, if only people . . .'

Yes, if only people had roses in their hearts there would be no more wars, no more misery, just beauty and goodness.

People who have never plucked a rose in their lives have heard of Harry Wheatcroft.

The rose was given by Cupid to Harpocrates, the god of silence, as a bribe not to betray the amours of Venus; hence the rose became the emblem of silence. It is wise to choose roses for your 'retreat' when you go there for silence and meditation. From this old legend originated the custom of suspending a rose from the ceiling at meetings where matters that demanded secrecy were discussed. And today we find the roses carved on the ceilings of council chambers, and in the sixteenth century it was placed over confessionals. What you say to your subconscious and what your subconscious says to you when you listen, during the meditation in your private little room, is something to be regarded as a secret. Try always to keep a rose there. It will help you to bring out the magic.

Roman emperors wishing to confer a special honour on their generals, would grant them permission to add a rose to the ornaments on their shields. And it is used by his Holiness the Pope when he desires to bestow special recognition on a church, sanctuary, or country.

You may have a garden full of flowers, but have you given serious thought to them? Roses have long been credited with many healing and curative qualities. There are more than thirty remedies compounded from their leaves and petals, and dew from the flowers has often been used as a 'cure' for inflamed eyes. Roses in the room of a drinker are said to ward off heavy drinking. When people become more alive to what flowers can do, the key to our forgotten healing powers will be turned in the door, which will open out on to infinity and wondrous new vistas. It is not for nothing that the **Rose of Life** is used by surgeons of the heart.

Snowdrops have a floromatic name. They are called **lights of the earth** and are said to bring good fortune into any place that has known ill-luck. If that isn't magic, what is?

And there are flowers that tell the time of day. Many flowers, like **pansies**, open at sunrise and close at sunset. But before the days of cheap watches, gardeners used to take notice of **convolvulus** to warn them that it was dinner-time. The **Star of Bethlehem** was nicknamed **Lady Eleven O'Clock**, because its flowers opened about that time. **Marigolds** go off to sleep about four p.m. and **water-lilies** begin to close at tea-time. **Night Scented Stock** opens about eight p.m. and closes at daybreak. There are many more flowers which tell the time, but I am not going into this now.

If you want to remove disharmony-within-creation or disharmony-within-your-environment, **turn to flowers**. As a result of many years' extensive study, two people with perfect attunement discovered a substance so potent it is capable of giving all created things the ability to re-orientate. This substance comes from flowers. They searched for a flower that would act as a **selector**. It was found, and it is the discovery of the age. In a booklet these two people say, 'Included in this substance are elements which provide a direct link-up with all the dimensions from the first to the fifth. It is effective no matter what the circumstances. Its power to readjust itself to individual needs is delicate, accurate, and unfailing.'

You want to overcome your fears, your anxieties, and be tolerant, gentle, and full of belief.

'A number of flowers possess these qualities in a vital and pure form,' they say, and these two people have communicated them to pure water in such a way that when the liquid is taken (a few drops only) these same qualities are strengthened within you. To take this liquid of the flowers is to experience deep and true exultation. It cures your ills, and it cures sick animals. And those who are already well are made more perfect. A little sprinkled on the ground makes flowers bloom with the most exquisite beauty and used for growing vegetables and fruit it improves flavour beyond description. And the booklet says: 'It increases the vitality of crops to such an extent that disease cannot affect them.' Tens of thousands have confirmed marvellous results.

And why all this magic? Well, flowers are fifth-dimensional and this is where you, who would work magic for yourself, must try to reach.

Is high-frequency life any different to what we experience? Indeed it is. This remarkable little booklet will tell you: 'In the high-frequency order of things, the more often you use, the more there is.' But it is the exact opposite in this life which is of a much lower frequency; the more you use, the less there is. Do remember this. Consequently, the more you use this liquid of the flowers which is of a higher-frequency and brings perfection, the more and more perfect and pure you become. Harmony and healing takes place, and the more whole you are, the easier is it for you to reach this fifth-dimensional plane – the plane where all is magic.

You may think all this is very far-fetched and impossible. That substance from flowers which have been specially prepared could not possibly cure your ills, or the sickness of your pet. You may shrug your shoulders at the idea that a few sprinkles on the ground could cause flowers, fruit, and vegetables to be more perfect. There are others like you. The Doubters.

A case was brought to Court over whether this substance was genuine or not, and whether it really worked. These two grand people won, hundreds of cures were proved, and the Flowers came out victorious.

There is magic in flowers, and you must concentrate on this. Why not send a box of flowers to someone, as a surprise? Don't look upon them as something to give to the dead only. Surround the living with colour and beauty, and let them get the benefit that flowers will give them.

You know a nation by its flowers. France by her packed masses of **Parma violets**, the United States by her **American beauty roses**, Holland by her straight, martial **tulips**, and England by the exquisite **sweet pea**.

And just as surely as you may know a nation by its flowers, so may you know human beings. Those who were sane and dear enough to send flowers to you when you were radiantly well, and alive, were men and women who transported you from **an unlovely world into a paradise**. They were among the best of people.

Oh, if only men and women would realize the beauty and help of flowers when you are alive! There are cities abroad where no lamp post exists without its hanging basket of brilliant blossoms. And there are towns in England which have adopted this scheme of decoration.

'If only somebody would send me some flowers,' you think. But it only seems to happen on films, or when you are dead.

You would thrill at the thought of seeing on the outside **Flowers with care**. You imagine yourself cutting the string, taking off the brown paper, lifting up the lid, gently catching hold of the white tissue.

What then? Ah, **violets** perhaps, or **roses**, pale pink **peonies** or **mimosa** and **maidenhair fern**. You picture the label with your name on it; the card inside with a few words of greeting.

Your little room would look beautiful with the passionate purity of the white flowers, crimson **tulips**, softly creased white blossoms tied in little bunches. The room would look wonderful.

You see golden petals, velvet purples, flowers of orange, and pink and white. There would be rich flowers, streaked with strange fantastic hues, starred branches dripping with yellow pom-pons. And in the centre of all this wonder, a magic card – **with your name on it!**

You look round your room. There they are. Your Mecca. So lovely.

You go from blossom to blossom like an enchanted butterfly, softly touching a petal, softly sniffing a double **narcissus**. It was not a small box, not just a few flowers. Many, many flowers – all the sweetness in the world was there. Your room is full of the most **exquisite** perfume. It is a beautiful pageant, the most splendid gift of radiance. It is like a beatitude. You are in a dream. You feel better already. You feel you want to throw your arms around everyone, you are so happy.

Yes, **magic**, that's what it would be.

Ludwig Feuerbach, the German philosopher, who declined to find a higher sanction for morality than man's own conception of wrong based on a doctrine of Hedonism, said:

'In the perishable petals of the flower there resides more spirit and life than in the lumpish granite boulder that has defied the tear and wear of thousands of years.'

Believe me, this is true.

I like the old Cockney saying, **'Stick a geranium in yer 'at and be 'appy.'**

Many of you have seen me talking to someone who has come up on the stage from the audience, and describes his **dream** car. (Anybody is free to come, and I ask for their names and addresses, so that there is no question of 'stooges'.)

I will ask, 'What sort of car would you like?' Then I will name the make, quickly, before the answer comes. And I am right.

'What colour car?'

But before the words come, I say **red**. 'That's it, isn't it?' Flabbergasted, he nods. I'm right again.

'You would like the registration number to be so-and-so?' I would.

'How much do you want to pay for it?' With a snap of the fingers, I name the figure. He looks puzzled. Admits I'm right.

'You will have a vase of flowers each side?'

Correct again. 'I've always wanted flowers in my car,' he replies.

'Good.' I feel in my breast pocket, and draw out a bill for the car. Same make, same colour, the same registration numbers. I hand it to him. For a moment he is speechless. He looks at it, then looks at me. 'How on earth did you know?'

Daily Express headline:

    'Al knows the answer – before you tell him.'

15
The Magic Of Right Habits

HABITS make you the person you are. So, unless you find yourself radiantly well, fascinating, prosperous, able to work magic and live gloriously, why not alter them now? As a psychologist and magician, the habit of perfection should be your first aim.

Poverty is the result of the wrong habits of thinking. You cannot have a negative vocabulary and expect to be anything else but poor; poor in health, poor in looks, poor in pocket. To break this habit, which can never bring out the magic in your mind, first cultivate a liking for **positive** words. Concentrate upon them and **use** them. Having begun to like **positive** words, you become word-conscious. And when you are word-conscious, you no longer use the words of a pauper. The world owes you nothing – nothing but a **chance.** This is your chance; your wonderful chance to break a bad habit and start using words that will bring magic into your life.

Forget the mistake you have been making in the past. Think of the opportunity that now presents itself to you; the habit of speaking positive words that awakens the sleeping magic in you. Discipline yourself to keep your words **positive.** You have been spending more time looking at the negation about you, than you have been spending in positive thoughts. The truest satisfaction, the deepest joy, the highest form of magic, comes from words spoken in a positive spirit.

All the knowledge in the world will not bring magic into your life unless you get into the habit of speaking only the right words. The Bible says, 'In the beginning was the word. . . .' The word is the important thing.

The word of Elias changed the waters, so that they were made to carry iron across their surface. The word of Moses divided the Red Sea.

Like the drunken Rip van Winkle in Jefferson's play, who excused himself for every mistake by saying, 'I won't count this time!' you may not count it when you are negative **just this once**, but it is being counted, all the same. Your subconscious counts it, registers it, stores it up, and uses it against you when the next wrong word is spoken. Nothing you ever say is wiped out. If it is the wrong word, it is used against you in stopping the magic you want. If it is the right word, it is used to your benefit, by bringing you that much nearer your magic goal. Your habits follow you, surround you, envelop you. As time goes on, the possibility of breaking a bad habit becomes more and more remote, until at last it is well-nigh impossible. If you are not working magic for yourself, recognize right now that you are speaking and thinking negative words. As time goes on, any such transition as a magic life becomes less and less likely.

Unless this terrible habit is halted soon, once and for all, you will experience irretrievable disaster. And in this hell of your own making, you will have no illusions. You will be aware that you wrote off the magic in your mind, when it might have been yours. You will know that you could have had the magic transformation of Cinderella or Aladdin, but that you flung it away. The man who walks finally away from the magic that could be his, walks at last into fire; the fire of his own hell.

Every now and again the sunlight will break through in

one place or another, and you will behave in a more con structive manner; you will use positive words. But it will be spasmodic unless you determine to make right words a daily habit, with no kind of wavering. Don't let your mind be overshadowed or you will become feeble as the result of your bad habits. Be aware of them, and clear the way for your subconscious to work for your good. The crucial step that makes all the difference – must be your own. Right habit formation will bring you magic every time.

From this moment onward, I want you to see yourself as you really want to be. Charming, prosperous, optimistic. Break down the habit of seeing yourself as someone who can accomplish nothing spectacular. Don't just wish. **Do something,** because **action** is necessary no matter what habit you desire to break. 'But I'm too old to break it now,' you say. There you go – negative, negative, negative. I know that habits are the very dickens to change, but some sacrifice and more action will do the trick. Don't make a trifling effort; make a gigantic determination.

'This fellow had begun to interest me,' you say, 'but what he wants me to do is the impossible. I can never do it.'

The word **never** should never be used in magic, except in the phrase, **'You never know'.**

No, you never know; you never know what you can do until you begin to try. I passionately repeat, you must break your bad habits.

To live on a new plane, and we are aiming at the highest, you must acquire new habits. You must become enthusiastic. Your manner of speaking must indicate authority, your thinking must be dynamic. Close your eyes and picture the **new you,** and break the habit right now. Like that you will enter a new life, full of magic.

One of the best habits to make, is to get up early in the morning. Progressive people who make fortunes, all get up very early; for many the day starts at 5 a.m. or 6 a.m. It is a habit with them, and one of the finest. You are not flying blind. All you are or shall be depends upon your habits.

How about your health? Are you making right habits there? The right habits will increase your health and energy amazingly, and will send you towards fitness in leaps and bounds. To an extent which will astonish you, your subconscious actions are directed by your daily habits; by what you do and think each day. Your lips may say, 'I want a fine physique, radiant health and a buoyant tread,' but if your subconscious mind knows from your daily habits that, as a matter of fact, you are really more interested in smoking heavily, taking the wrong drinks, and never exercising in the open air, then that is what you will get. Your underneath mind carefully weighs all your words and actions. It puts two and two together, and if your words and actions are not in harmony you can never attain a strong, bronzed body and springing step.

So be careful about your health habits. Fan the flame of your worthwhile habits; those occasions when you opened the window to practise deep breathing, and that memorable day when you got up a little earlier and took a brisk walk over the hill with the dog before breakfast.

Fresh air is invigorating, and drives your subconscious mind irresistibly to seek more and more joyous exercise, more and more fresh air, in its efforts to secure for you that strong, healthy body for which you have long craved.

You cannot break a bad habit by affirming, 'I won't do so-and-so any more.' You will not make much progress if you say 'I won't.' Deliberately prepare a new and infinitely more desirable radiant health habit. Say what you will do, that's the thing. You will join the gymnasium club with Bill. You will take your dog for a brisk walk before breakfast every morning. You will eat salads and wholemeal bread, and study the right foods, despite the ridicule of those of your fellow creatures who know little or nothing about radiant living.

Impress your mind with what you are **going to do**. Straighten your neck, tense your muscles vigorously, and breathe fully and deeply, rhythmically, as you vow that you will be the master of your life, and work magic.

It is absolutely essential to adopt a schedule, and to drum these new radiant health habits you are going to practise, into your ears and eyes. There is no easy, haphazard road to health. It has to be deeply concentrated upon and worked for. Anyone who promises you an easy road to health is leading you down a blind alley.

Visualize yourself as being bronzed and physically fit and handsome. Fix a picture of some beautiful figure you admire in front of you as you exercise, and concentrate on having a similar body. Think of the life-giving fresh air reaching your lungs as you breathe more fully. You will begin to feel, 'I can do great things.'

Write down the things you are going to do in order to attain new vitality and radiant health. **Write them on paper.** Keep a little note-book for the purpose. Read them every day, **think** them, **dream** them, **act** them, **be** them, until these radiant health habits dominate and govern your life.

Drive the idea of sun-bathing, air-bathing, muscular development, massage, non-smoking, deep breathing, right diet, and other necessary habits for health into your mind daily, through as many different senses as possible.

Write them out (muscular, eye impressions).

Read them out aloud (muscular impressions through the lips, eye and ear impressions).

Act them out.

See yourself joining a health club.

See yourself exposing your body each day to fresh air and sun-rays (real or artificial) if only for a quarter of an hour.

See yourself with a strong, bronzed body, charged full of energy and power.

Collect pictures of handsome nude and semi-nude men and women in poses that depict superb beauty and radiance, and focus your attention upon these pictures continually. Determine to be like unto. With all the conviction and determination you can muster, swear by all that you ever hope to achieve that nothing will content you but a vision of yourself as radiantly fit and perfect as the pictures you so ardently admire.

The best habit of all, and the one which makes good habits, graciousness, and beauty a mathematical certainty is the habit of holding unwaveringly in your mind only those mental pictures and patterns which you wish to become true in your life.

Repetition is absolutely essential. As far as habits are concerned, it is repetition which establishes them. Repeat over and over and over again the things you desire, until they finally become fixed in your mind and heart, a guiding, controlling impression in your mind, leading you on to radiant health and beauty, and all the magic you wish.

Let us recap on some of the things I have said. Have you established **Belief**, or are you still in doubt?

Is sleeping with your head to the North a habit with you now? Have you got into the habit of crossing your legs, and closing your hands when you want to cut off bad vibrations?

Do you visualize all that you want every day, and is it a daily habit with you to look at the pictures of these things in your book? Remember I told you to paste pictures in a book.

Have you made filling your rooms with flowers a habit? And what about good music? Do you hear music every day?

Is going into the silence a habit yet? Don't put it off a day longer. It should be a regular habit to go into your retreat and think.

Are you on speaking terms with your subconscious, and do you listen for guidance? If you have not made this a daily habit by now, you will never bring out the magic in your mind.

How about Love. Is this a very real part of your life? Do you send out thoughts of love each day, and are you now in the habit of loving and blessing your enemies?

Do you tithe? Whenever you get money, do you make it a habit to put ten per cent aside, for the benefit of the sick and poor? Is the Law of Riches well remembered, and as you use your money every day, are you in the habit of blessing it?

What are you doing about colour in your life? Is it a habit with you to always wear something bright, and have you changed the dull things in your home, to colour, so that you may have the benefit of high vibrations?

What about the habit of making new friends? How many new friends have you made since you began to read this book?

All these things must become right habits in your life, if you want to work magic. Make a habit of picking up this book every day, and re-reading a portion of it to impress your subconscious. Even if you think you can remember all that has been written, still read again, for it is repetition that makes for success; the continual hammering away, so that it becomes your most precious habit of all.

You want to work magic? Work for it, every hour, every minute, in the daily habits of your life. You have a golden opportunity, don't throw it away.

If you are in the habit of seeing me on stage or television, I am very glad. I like to baffle you.

Extract from **The Bulletin.**

'. . . But if you've seen Al work on TV or the stage and been completely puzzled, don't worry too much. No less a person than the late Professor Einstein failed to find out how it's done.'

The professor was fascinated by a demonstration I gave him in London.

16
The Magic Of
Music

To the average man, music consists of a succession of sounds arranged harmoniously for our entertainment. The mysterious influence of music – its deeper effect – is hardly felt consciously, and so man remains strangely ignorant and unmindful of the magic power that music has.

I want you to realize this tremendous fact from the very beginning, you are continually affected, adversely or otherwise, by the vibrations of music which surround you. If you would live happily, realizing all your dreams, remember that music is a channel through which the Law of Harmony works, and as such, may be used as a channel to better health, peace, love, and aspiration. Perverted 'music' with its erratic rhythms and jarring discords which blare out to you from the radio, juke boxes and the like, can actually cause unbalanced emotions of a primitive nature; fear, aggressiveness, and so on. The vibrations from this type of 'music' can damage the nervous system for good, if you hear too much of it.

Your choice in music can decide what dimension you can reach, and what help you can get. Listen only to those presentations that really inspire, that are harmonious, soft, and lovely. You can banish negative conditions with this sort of music, but not with the jerky, jazzy kind.

If you are depressed or mentally sick, the value of tone harmonies cannot be sufficiently emphasized. The sound of a beautiful melody can solve many a complicated situation, nor does its influence end there. Its power is versatile and extends over a variety of mental and physical and even spiritual distresses.

If you long for a simple road to the inner awakening of magic, choose the right music and weave it closely into your life-pattern.

Be careful about the music you allow to enter your consciousness, for the tonal qualities aid or hinder your power to work magic, far more than you realize. Discordant 'music' is not for you; somebody hits somebody with a bottle, that's the way it is. It does not make for peace and harmony, it affects the mind in a bad way, whether one realizes it or not.

The world today needs harmony. Do not play on the strings of life out of tune. Listen to the music of beautiful voices, the song of a bird, the mighty strains of an orchestra, the plaintive tones of a sweet melody as if tomorrow you would be stricken deaf. Use your ears as never before. You must let music become dear to you. Harmony is the basis of beautiful music, and harmony is the basis of a beautiful life.

I know a lady who was anxious that her unborn child should have a love of music when it was born. Whenever she relaxed she sent the unborn child thoughts of music and love of music. Then she would play beautiful music on the record-player. The child eventually born to her had a great soul for music, and by the time it was old enough to play the piano, soon became a brilliant musician. Likewise, you can talk to the subconscious of a sleeping child, regularly each night, desiring it to love good music, and the day will come when this is so, for the subconscious never fails.

It has been recorded that recently doctors tested a number of babies' reaction to a mother's heart-beat.

The soft, beating sound was played to them, and they fell asleep contented. It was good music to them. As soon as the music stopped they awoke and cried. There is no lovelier music to a baby than the sound of its mother's heart-beat. They are soothed by it.

A big china musical pig helped little children to survive the awful tragedy of the ill-fated **Titanic**. The music of the pig helped to stop the children crying, keeping up their spirits until rescue came. This true story was told by Edith Russell, an American visiting London, who was a first-class passenger on the **Titanic**. The music worked magic for those children.

A man, on discovering that his potted ivy curled over at the leaf-edges, wondered if his Dizzy Gillespie L.P. was driving it mad. He approached Cyril Scott, the composer, who believes that plants react sensitively to music.

He suggests that you can tone them up by playing something sympathetic, and that you disturb them terribly with neurotic jazz. You may think this is crazy, but I believe it is quite possible. I respect Cyril Scott, whose works influenced Elgar and Debussy. 'I have heard that if you subject plants to a sustained note of C, they flourish,' he says. C is very suitable for plants. An American researcher studying the effects of playing a gramophone in a field of wheat, discovered that music in the distance had a very good effect on the wheat, but very near, it had a disturbing effect. Try rearing your plants with Debussy's **'Gardens in the Rain'**.

The Himalayans give you **sound** to concentrate on. The name of the sound must never pass your lips. But when you want to relax you listen to it. And when you get really good at listening you can get in touch with the super-conscious.

It may not be so long before you are offered music as an alternative to anaesthetic.

Already many people in America and some in this country have had teeth extracted without a local anaesthetic. Instead, they have had the soft, soothing music of the classics. There has never been a whimper from those in the chair.

Doctors who have carried out these experiments believe that music is felt in the same part of the brain that responds to pain. They believe that the sound of music can block off the brain's reaction to pain by 'jamming' the signals from the nerve centres which are affected. Such is the magic of music.

I know a woman of eighty-five who always plays the piano **before breakfast!** She looks remarkably younger than her years, and I am sure this has had something to do with it. She starts the day right, and in harmony.

'I am about to leave my wife,' a man once said to me. 'When we were married she seemed a perfect wife. Now, after only two years, we are through – only she doesn't know it yet. I shall go home tonight, as usual, and switch on the radio. She will moan, "I'm fed up with music."

'I will start reading. She will moan, "You always stick your nose in a book." '

Then he said, 'I shall lay the book down and switch on the music again. She will moan, "Music, music – I'm sick of it!"

'And then I shall walk out. I'm fed up with her continual moaning about music.'

Are you a Beat fan? Music it may be, of a kind, but it is not the least bit helpful to you as far as magic is concerned. It is a raw kind of music, usually played by those with a beatnik style of appearance; tight jeans and black leather jackets. This earthy type of music can send you silly, if you listen to enough of it.

Can music cure sick minds? Good music, I mean. If mental patients listen consistently to good music, can it eventually calm them into normality?

Hephzibah Menuhin, the concert pianist and sister of violinist Yehudi Menuhin, claims that it can. 'Music is a mysterious thing, like the mind,' she says. 'Perhaps that is why I have found it a language that speaks directly to even lost minds.'

Between concerts and recording sessions, Hephzibah spends much time in mental hospitals, playing, singing, and talking to patients. She mixes even with dangerous lunatics in her belief that she can cure through music.

In Australia, three hospitals have paid tribute to this novel approach to mental patients which, unlike the dangerous medical methods of so many drugs, may prove to be a humane contribution to the constructive treatment of mental illness.

I absolutely agree with Yehudi Menuhin's sister. Music is the finest tranquillizer there is. I have often caught myself thinking, so-and-so has started to look unhappy. He is unhappy either because he is mentally disturbed, or he is going to become mentally disturbed because he is unhappy. Whatever your age, the real key to your health is **a state of happiness** – and nothing makes for happiness more than music of the right kind. Debussy once said: **'To music only is it given to capture all the poetry of night and day and of the earth and of the heavens, to reconstruct the atmosphere, then record the rhythm of the heart-beats.'**

Many people will doubt Hephzibah's idea of music being a cure for the sick mind, but if you believe that music can get your mind well again, it will.

In Beethoven's case, music was a challenge to his deafness, which he accepted and over which he triumphed to his enduring glory. The power and magic of music should never be underrated. I think Martin Luther summed it up very truly when he said that **'music makes people milder and gentler, more moral and more reasonable'.**

Music is our fourth great material need – first food, then clothes, then shelter, then **music.**

To quote Martin Luther again: **'Music is the art of the prophets – the only art which can calm the agitations of the soul. Where you have no agitation of the soul, you have no sickness of the mind.'**

People need to occupy their hands if they would get their minds better. The physical employment of the hands at an instrument, in conjunction with the mental employment of producing music, cannot but have the most beneficial effect upon anyone whose nervous system is slightly disturbed. More than this, I think that since music must be recognized

174

as a message to the spirit, there must be a host of mental sufferers whose condition may well have come about simply because they have not heard all the music that they should have done. Deny the soul what it needs, and our minds become sick; slowly, inevitably, we go all to pieces unless something is done about it.

Music leads us to a higher plane, and it works magic. Many cases could be quoted to assure you of this, but for the moment let me tell you about young Lloyd Franklin.

Only three years ago, Lloyd, a boyish-looking Londoner, sang for his supper because he was broke. Yes, he was penniless. He became a dishwasher in a London coffee bar for fifteen shillings a night. But he had a guitar and guts. He went abroad as a courier and swotted at the language rather than have fun dancing to flamenco music. He was that poor.

Somebody heard him playing his guitar and invited him to a party where famous people were present. And that was how he met the Woolworth heiress, Barbara Hutton. His music excited her and her eyes never left him. That was how one of the richest women in the world came to make a close friend of Lloyd Franklin.

Now a super-luxury bachelor flat is being prepared for him in Paris.

He flies around the world in a private plane.

He has a Rolls-Royce embellished with his regimental crest – he was once in Her Majesty's Life Guards.

He lives in splendour in a secluded bungalow in sun-soaked Africa and among his friends are princes and millionaires, screen stars and television idols. As long as he lives he will never have to worry about money any more.

The flamenco music he played on his battered old guitar worked magic – because it attracted Barbara Hutton, who from that moment turned his life into a fairy tale.

I have told you how flowers work magic, how colour works magic, and now give thought to music. It worked magic for Lloyd Franklin, and it can work magic for you.

It even works magic for the cows in the farmyard, for we are told that, when milked to music, they give more and better milk.

Farmer W. J. Roberts, of Barrow, Suffolk, had 1,500 pigs and they fought so much that he was worried. They wouldn't fatten quickly enough. Now he gives them the Light programme on the radio all day; they listen to the Archers, Beethoven and dance music, and he says they are now **very contented**. It has solved his problem and worked magic with the pigs.

Gerald Parkinson, the well-known artist, gets inspiration for his paintings from music. When he's working on a **stormy** picture he likes to hear Rimsky-Korsakov or Sibelius; when it's a subject which calls for a calm mood, he is soothed and helped by Debussy or Chopin. The Twist leaves him cold; nothing can be gained from this type of music unless it is a nervous breakdown!

A lady told me the other day that she always listened to the music of Menotti. 'It helps me so much,' she said.

Am I helped by music? Before I give a performance of magic, I listen to music in my dressing-room. I attach great importance to music. My favourite composers are **Puccini, Rimsky-Korsakov, Lehar, Verdi,** and the uncrowned king of Vienna, **Johann Strauss.** I have a large collection of long-playing records which can nearly always be heard playing, whether I am at home, or back-stage.

17
Have Done With Fear

FEAR was front-page news four thousand years ago! It was in the headlines when Noah launched the Ark. It appears four hundred and one times in the Bible. It has predominated through every war, and when there is no war, we are still afraid of something or somebody.

It is fatal for any magician to have fear. If you are afraid, you cannot work magic. The two are foreign to each other. Fear is negative, and therefore unworkable.

Some know the meaning of claustrophobia (fear of confined spaces). They cannot phone from a public booth, they cannot ride for long in small cars, they cannot sit in a non-corridor train, the middle row in a cinema, or even in a room unless the door is open.

If this applies to you, you would give the earth to know how to overcome it.

Agoraphobia is the opposite: a fear of open spaces. If you have to cross the road you are sure you will get knocked down, or collapse when you are half-way over. You are terrified of being out alone where space is all around you. What can you do about it? You shrink and cower, expecting something unknown to strike you. You don't think there is anything that can cure you of this fear.

177

Ailourophobia – the fear of cats, strikes panic in you, although you are fond of animals. Field-Marshal Lord Roberts, V.C., couldn't even bear to look at pictures of cats, much less have one near him.

Another terror Astrapophobia – fear of strong winds. You must stay indoors when there is a gale, you dare not venture out. You are afraid the wind will choke you or bowl you over, or that trees and things will fall on you.

Hematophobia – fear of blood, is a dreadful thing, for even a pinprick that draws a spot of blood makes you feel faint. Butcher shops are torture chambers to you, because the sight of blood is too much. You can't stand it.

Have you ever leaned out of a third-floor window and looked below? Climbed a hill, and looked down? You can't do it. This mysterious horror is Acrophobia – fear of heights. They seem to draw you. It affects some people very deeply; they dare not stand on a chair, because they become really ill.

Hydrophobia – fear of water, means that you are unable to enjoy a sea view, for the water seems to call to you. You have to keep away.

Fear of the dark – called Nyctophobia, makes you turn around every few minutes at night, because you feel someone is behind you.

Perhaps you are afraid of crowds; of being alone; of leaving the house; of meeting people. Whichever form your fear takes, it sits on your shoulder like a bird of prey, and holds you back from magic. You want to run away, but your legs are like lead. You panic, your heart beats wildly, you perspire. Your constant battle against fear is exhausting. You have been reading this book and thought you could work magic, but now you feel you can't. You hadn't thought about **fear**. You had not reckoned to contend with **that**. Your conflicting emotions give rise to muzziness. Clear thinking is impossible; all of a sudden you feel unreal. You may have mastered all I've said, but you can't see how you can get rid of fear, not even by magic.

What is the solution? First, realize that your feeling of fear is your heaviest burden. Talk to your subconscious. Listen to your subconscious. You will probably hear something like this: **What you are most afraid of won't happen.** Act on it. Take courage from it. Put fear out of your mind. Be positive. You want to work magic and you **can** work magic, if you determine to have done with fear.

How can you best get rid of 'being afraid'? By **belief.** Believe in your subconscious. As I told you previously, your subconscious **knows everything.** Past, present, and future. **Yes, everything.** Your subconscious protects you; warns you of impending danger; guides you the way you should go.

You have a premonition. That comes from your subconscious. I told you that I once had a premonition not to accept a lift home from the theatre in a friend's car. I acted on it, and saved myself from being in a terrible crash. I had a **feeling;** an impression, a hunch – call it what you will – and this came from my subconscious who was warning me. You will get a **feeling,** a strong impression, if you regularly talk and listen to your subconscious. Like this you will be warned and guided. You will be protected. Everybody gets warnings, but few recognize them, as they are not **aware** of their subconscious and the wonderful mental radio within their own minds. You must be **aware** of the power of your subconscious and not be asleep at the switch. Like this, you become guarded and protected. There is no need to fear **anything,** when you have this knowledge. You need never be afraid of thunderstorms; need not feel terror when it lightens. Your subconscious can warn you long before the approach of a storm, if you should stay where you are or flee elsewhere. You think this impossible? Listen:

A large number of birds made their daily roost at the top of a big tree. You could always see them congregated there.

But one particular day they were not to be seen. They did not sit at the top of the tree as was their usual habit. **That tree was struck by lightning.** The birds knew it was going to be struck. They knew they had not to go to that tree as usual

And in like manner, we are not left high and dry. We get premonitions. Like the birds, we must **act**.

We are all warned, the thing is to be **aware**. Ken Lawton, who is a brilliant dancer, a fine singer and an accomplished actor, who has appeared in a dozen or so West End shows, including **Annie Get your Gun, Love from Judy**, and **Irma La Douce** – was certainly warned. He was travelling from London up North, and was just in time to catch his train. It was important that he caught that train, as he had to be on time for the show. But he had a **feeling** that he mustn't go on it, and he **acted** upon this impression. There was a terrible rail crash and very many people on that train were killed.

Horatio Nelson, the greatest sailor since our world began, (Tennyson's words, not mine) had great **awareness**, and always knew what was going to happen. It started when he was in his teens. He had fits of depression and said he 'wished himself overboard'.

Southey, in his **Life of Nelson**, comments on this depression: **'The state of mind in which these feelings began is what the Mystics mean by their season of darkness and desertion.'**

Several years later, when he was a Captain commanding **H.M.S. Albemarle** off the coast of America, his subconscious mind **knew**, and he **acted on it**.

He had just captured a fishing schooner owned and commanded by Master Nathaniel Carver, homeward bound for Boston. By the rules of war the schooner was now Nelson's prize – to bring him much-needed prize-money with which to help support an aged father and several younger brothers and sisters. But acting on this strange inward prompting, he threw this to the winds of destiny!

Sending for Carver, he ordered him to pilot both vessels into Boston Bay. This done, Nelson restored the schooner and her cargo to the speechless master, giving him a certificate to prevent his capture by any other British ship!

Then came swift Karma! Nelson and his crew, weakened by battling against strong gales and salt food, fell victims to a dreaded and often fatal disease. Nelson decided to land his worst victims at Quebec for treatment.

Suddenly, through the mist, a sail was seen approaching them. They were hailed, and alongside came the fishing schooner with Master Nathaniel Carver at her wheel. In the thick of the most deplorable war he had risked his life and ship to bring Nelson presents of fresh fruit, vegetables, and poultry!

These gifts, coming at the moment when they did, saved the lives of Nelson and his crew. And all this, because Nelson **acted** upon his **feelings.** Did his subconscious **warn** him of impending illness? Did his subconscious **persuade** him to give away the schooner, in order that it may come to his rescue? You can look at it how you like, but it appears to be so, doesn't it?

And then again, seated with his officers at dinner whilst cruising off the mouth of the Nile, word was brought to the cabin that the French fleet had been sighted in Aboukir Bay, just ahead of them.

Without asking their strength or disposition, Nelson calmly remarked: **'By this time tomorrow, I shall have gained a peerage or Westminster Abbey!'**

In due course he was raised to the peerage as Baron Nelson of the Nile and of Burnham Thorpe! Again, his **feeling** proved right.

Again, an old Nile friend of the Admiral, Capt. The Hon. Henry Blackwood, arrived at Nelson's Surrey home early in September. He found Nelson already up and dressed and strolling in the garden, although it was only five in the morning!

Nelson walked eagerly up to him as he drove in. He said: **'I'm sure you bring me news of the French and Spanish fleets! I'm sure I have yet to beat them!'** How did he know? He was ashore on sick-leave and his Squadron at sea. There were no radios and televisions. It came from his own mind. He was **warned**.

Always, his **feelings** proved correct. 'Depend upon it, Blackwood,' said Nelson, 'I shall yet give Monsieur Villeneuve a drubbing!' and again it proved true. After accepting the command from the First Lord, Nelson acted on another impression. Leaving the Admiralty, he went straight to his upholsterer's where was stored the coffin, made from the mainmast of **L'Orient**, Flagship of the French at the Nile, and given him as a grim memento of that action.

He requested his upholsterer to take out of storage the coffin and have its history engraved upon it, saying that he would **most probably require it on his return**.

In due course he put to sea in his beloved Flagship **Victory** and rejoined his Squadron cruising off Cadiz; and although the enemy ships could be seen there, each preparing for sea, Nelson's **feelings** told him that the time for action was not yet.

Some of his ships needed stores, and were sent to Gibraltar for that purpose. But one captain feared he would miss the battle. Nelson smiled confidently and said: **'There'll be plenty of time for you to go to Gibraltar and return,'** and he was right again!

An excited group of midshipmen on the **Victory's** quarter-deck were eagerly discussing the chances of battle and promotion. They had overheard the Admiral talking with Captain Hardy, who expressed his wonder if the enemy put to sea that day. Nelson, walking over to the group of lads, said with his strange sad smile: **'Tomorrow will be a fortunate day for you, young gentlemen, but I will not live to see it.'**

Next morning the opposing fleets were sailing firmly towards each other. The seamen stowed away pictures and furniture in the Admiral's cabin and glanced at one another. On his desk lay discarded his 'fighting sword', comrade of all his former actions. For the first time in his career, Nelson had gone into battle without his sword! What did it mean?

182

Blackwood had taken his hand and said he hoped to return after the battle and find him in possession of twenty prizes.

Nelson shook his head. 'God bless you, Blackwood. I shall never speak to you again!'

Blackwood returned later to find his Admiral already speechless, sinking into a coma. Nelson had known. And he had been right again!

Doesn't it go to show that your mind is truly wonderful? That you can rely upon your subconscious to tell you things – true things, never untruths – is proved again and again. Why are you afraid of gales, water, open spaces, confined spaces, and all the rest of it? Simply because of what might happen. Yet if anything awful was going to happen to you, you would be warned. All you've got to do is practise meditation, quietly listening in, so that you can cultivate that certain feeling which you get when trouble is on the map. The more you meditate, the more do you become able to feel things.

By meditation you can train yourself to reach the fourth and fifth dimensions, the dimensions that cut out fear and give you calm. It was Job who said, 'The thing I feared has come upon me.' Of course it does, because you attract it.

Fear is out-of-focus thought. Who says so? That brilliant psychologist Gilbert Oakley, D.Psy., D.Sc., in his vital psychology book How to Cultivate Confidence and Promote Personality. He says in it, 'I fear nothing. Least of all do I fear being afraid. I know there is no such thing as fear. I know there is reasonable sense of precaution, care, and common sense. I see everything in its correct perspective and right proportion. This being so, I have no need of fear. . . .'

When you lack confidence you are fearful. It is self-confidence that you want.

I have thought about fear in all its most awful moments, and it has struck me that a man who could be calm in a terrible earthquake must surely have learned something.

So I read all about it. Sessue Hayakawa, who played Colonel Saito in The Bridge on the River Kwai, tells the story in his wonderful autobiography Zen showed me the way. Here is an extract:

'Some years ago, a European College Professor visiting in Japan was walking with some Japanese on the fifth floor of an hotel in Tokyo. Suddenly they all heard a rumbling. "There was a gentle heaving under our feet," the European later noted. The swaying and creaking and the crash of objects became more and more pronounced. Alarm and excitement mounted. The terror was all the greater because the great Japanese earthquake of 1923 was still fresh in memory. People rushed out of the room into the corridor to the stairs. Professor Eugene Herrigel, the European Professor, asked the Japanese gentleman with whom he had been talking why he didn't hurry to run for safety. "I noticed to my astonishment," Professor Herrigel said, "that he was sitting there unmoved, hands folded, eyes nearly closed, as though none of it concerned him."

. . . The Japanese who had remained so unperturbed was a Zen Buddhist. He had put himself into a state of extreme concentration and thus became unassailable.'

Why do I tell you this from what is one of the very finest books you could read? Because the philosophy of Buddhism is the nearest thing I know to psychology. A psychologist who studies Buddhism sees the likeness at once. As Sessue so truly says, 'In this day of fear – fear of atomic blast, radiation poisoning, annihilating war – we greatly need the ability to become individually "unassailable".'

Sessue Hayakawa is out to perfect his own mind. Is it not time that we perfected our own minds? We can free our minds of fear and put in its place perfect tranquillity. We can make ourselves 'unassailable'. When we reach the fourth dimension of mind, we can be unassailable. We would not feel fear. You will have noticed that the Japanese who had remained so unperturbed put himself in a state of extreme concentration. Concentrate upon the fourth dimension and so raise your mind. You will know no fear.

A newspaper heading said, 'So Bombs, or No Bombs, the

184

Queen is going to Ghana.' The Queen never shows a trace of panic. She is an extremely cool, and courageous person. She smiles her way through the densest crowd with never a thought of fear; of some fanatic throwing a bomb. Calm, courage and confidence, these are the lessons she teaches us. Think about it. Enlightenment will come.

The mind can see an event years and even centuries in the future. It can see an event only a few hours ahead. By acting on your premonition, or **feeling**, though you do not know **why** you should do so, it will be revealed soon.

Most people are afraid of something, be it anxiety over an ailing child, fear of losing someone's love, or of being left alone and unwanted. Fears that chill you. Fears of sickness, old age, and poverty. This is a terrible frame of mind to get into. Rise triumphant over your baser self. Your thoughts can be unforeseen obstacles in everything you do. They can be so powerful at times, that they can set in motion the very thing you fear, which accounts for the old saying that if you dread a thing, it happens. Your life begins to go wrong from the moment you fear it will do so. Your own anxiety causes an attitude which impels the thing you fear to happen. Carlyle said: 'The first duty of a man is that of subduing fear; he must get rid of fear; he cannot act at all till then, his acts are slavish, not true.'

You must get rid of fear, as Carlyle so truly says. To be told that something frightened us in our childhood and that is why we are frightened now, is no consolation. It may be the cause of our fear, this childhood memory, but what we are most concerned with is how to get rid of this awful feeling of being afraid.

You can do it through the training of your subconscious; through being so in tune with it that you can **recognize** the warnings given, or the message that brings courage. You can overcome fear like the pilots do. When they crash, they quickly go up in an aeroplane again, because if they didn't, they know they would never fly again. If you are afraid of the dark, you must go out in the dark as often as you can and face up to it. The fear will go. You cannot run away from what you fear, that only makes you more afraid. You must face it, I repeat.

There are instances where gamblers who are losing heavily and fear they will lose the lot, get up from the chair and draw a white chalk circle round it. This, they feel, protects them from evil, and the chances are they will start to win. But a white circle drawn round a man can hardly protect him from any harm, physically or mentally. The practice is just a psychological make-up to give confidence. It has no magic significance whatever. Practices such as this will only yoke a man to harmful beliefs. We should meditate more and grow into a state of inner tranquility if we would discard fears and limitations.

To prove that you **can** work magic, you must show that **you** are not afraid. You have **thought** yourself into that fear **with your mind**. Run yourself out of it with your legs.

You are ready to take your first dive, poised on the plank, leaning forward. You hesitate. Fear takes a hold of you. You try again and again. In the end you plunge, with a terrific flop. Because someone had laughed at you, and you couldn't bear it. So you dived, rather awkwardly, but you made the attempt at last.

Again and again you must plunge into the very thing that makes you afraid, and in the end you will have killed fear forever. Use your fear as a means of conquest. Very often a fear is due to using your mind more than your body. There should be **balance**. You generate fears if you think too much, and neglect action. Lead a more active life, exercise in the open, go for long walks. An overactive mind and an underactive body can only bring trouble. Take the longest walk you've ever taken, and **take this book with you**. Whilst you are reading, open it haphazard and read a few inspiring words. Then take the long walk home. Like that you have **balance**, the mind and body working in harmony. It is when

186

you get too much of one thing and not enough of the other, that you begin to run off the rails. **And that is how fear starts.**

Have I had fears? Yes, many of them. I have done a lot of parachuting, but being shot down **twice** over **enemy** territory was not so funny. But as I said before, when I was a nervous wreck in hospital for nine months, I overcame my illness and my fears completely, **through the study of psychology.** The pile of books on my bed **changed my life,** and I hope this book will happily change yours. The art of a magician is **transformation.**

18
The Magic Of Happiness

IT has been said that in America, where there is so much crime and drug-taking, one out of every twenty people are unbalanced. Stand in any queue in this country, and you see drawn faces, the harassed look of people who are wanting things and not getting them. You hear so much pessimistic talk, and know that most of them live on sleeping tablets and other pain-killing drugs. So you might say that it is the same here; about one in twenty have run off the rails.

I was talking to a railway booking clerk the other day, and he told me how he sold a laughing schoolgirl a ticket. 'You see few smiles through my little window,' he added.

Then he went on, 'We **are** a gloomy lot on the whole, don't you think?' he said.

I knew what he meant, for as a mind-reader and a man who observes people, I have noticed more scowls than smiles.

Yes, the majority of people are unhappy. They may be bright to a certain extent, but inside of them, they are unhappy, they are not 'glad all over' as the song says, and this leads people to do strange things.

Sometime today, somewhere, someone will be caught stealing for no apparent reason. Shoplifting is done so often by people who could well afford to buy things. They are not in desperate need.

However wrong stealing is, even the taking of petty things, it lends excitement to the wrong-doer. If they were happy, that in itself would be exciting, but they are not, so they thieve. They become unbalanced.

You cannot know happiness if you are unbalanced. You cannot know happiness if you do wrong, because even if you are not fully conscious that you are doing wrong, **your subconscious knows,** and it is this underneath mind that works the magic of happiness. You can't work magic by wrongdoing. It is against the law of **purity.** As I have said before, the first principle is **to be pure,** like the Fire Walkers, who would never attempt to walk barefoot over red-hot cinders until they had first become **pure.** You can't bring the magic out of your mind by taking sleeping pills and tranquillizers. Drugs dope the mind and put it out of action.

If happiness lasts no longer with you than a cloud's flight over the sun, then something is very wrong in your world.

What makes people happy? Is it a matter of money, health, success, romance, religion, or what? Or is it a matter of outlook?

It is a combination of all these things. I know it isn't easy to be happy when you can never make ends meet, when you are sick in mind and body because of it, when you can't get beyond the bottom rung of the ladder, when love has jilted you, or when you have no religion or philosophy to hang on to.

You are frustrated.

This book tells you how to get all these things right in your life; by meditation and visualization and right direction. You may be irritated to the extreme by bad conditions, but if you keep your attitude positive, you can overcome and achieve. Remember this, **the happy oyster with nothing to irritate him, is not the oyster who produces the pearl.**

If I haven't answered your problems, the Bible will. The

Bible is good psychology; it is full of wisdom on how to attain joy (happiness).

And what is its answer? **Belief.** Over and over again **two words** are used. **One thing. One thing** is lacking – faith. If you would bring the magic out of your mind; the magic which will transform everything, you must **believe.**

Whatever your condition, you can be happy if you have the right attitude, and train yourself to look at life through rose-coloured glasses.

The story of Cinderella is really the story of magic. Cinderella was the drudge of the home, but she never once complained. She never grumbled or criticized her Ugly Sisters. **She was happy.** She was sweetness. She had the right attitude. The Good Fairy (we will call her the subconscious who knew what Cinderella wanted) changed the pumpkin into a golden coach, the mice into horses, and Cinderella went to the Ball as glamorous as a Princess.

Cinderella was happy, even in rags. She went from rags to riches, because this attitude works magic. The subconscious can only do its work when the path is clear.

As you are training to be a magician, you should by now know the secret of happiness. You should have trained yourself to **believe,** you should have trained yourself to take your troubles to your subconscious in the quietude of your own little meditation room, you should have trained yourself to see wonderful things and to have the right attitude. You should have trained yourself to be **pure.**

It was Buddha who said: '**If a man speaks or acts with a pure thought, happiness follows him like a shadow that never leaves him.'**

If you adhere to this law of magic, this shadow will never leave you. You will always be happy. **Abracadabra** (speak the blessing).

This is how you bring the magic out of your mind. Seeing everything through rose-coloured glasses is the right attitude.

Tommy Steele, that polished, all-round performer, zestful

and exuberant, once said, **'I'm a firm believer that if a man's been happy up to twenty, he'll always be happy.'**

See what I mean? The right attitude.

A selfish person may know pleasure, riding here and there in his smart car, but such a person can never know happiness. A selfish person never goes out of his way to help you; he wouldn't give you a lift in his car no matter how many parcels you were carrying. Because such a thought never enters his silly head. He may have pleasures in plenty and boast of them (We're flying to Paris next week-end), but he doesn't know happiness which is something deeper and of the spirit.

There is an old Hindu proverb:

'Help thy brother's boat across and lo! thine own has reached the shore.'

In other words, it is the unselfish person who attracts magic and for whom it never leaves.

'Well,' you say, 'I've filled up the coal bucket for that old lady down the road, I've posted letters for that old pensioner across the way, I've baby-sat so that a young couple could go to a dance together, but what have I got? Nothing. Things are just the same as ever they were, there's nothing magical about it.'

If you do a kindness simply hoping to get something out of it, then you don't know the first thing about magic.

Walt Disney, in a recent film, created **Pollyanna,** the girl who takes the grimness out of life by **finding something to be glad about** in every situation. And that is the spirit of every magician.

'We never live, but we hope to live; and as we are always **arranging** for being happy it cannot be but that we never are so,' wrote Pascal.

You can't **arrange** to be happy. You don't **plan** it, just like that. **Happiness is an attitude of mind;** and you either have it or you have not. It happens if you have the right mind. If you planned to be happy tomorrow or the next day, there is no saying that it would be so, not unless you had the right

191

attitude **whatever happened**; if it rained, snowed, or the earth quaked. You don't **pursue** happiness. You don't run after it, like that. Happiness is something that fills the moment and it comes upon you unawares, while you are helping others. It's not something you **arrange**.

Emerson was a happy man, he must have been. In one of his diaries he says that his railway bonds crashed in the panic of 1657. He refers to his losses **just once**. His house burned down and his diary records **House burned**. Then he goes on to tell of the more important things for which he was ever grateful.

William Wilberforce kept a diary, too. He was not free from heartaches. He had a thousand and one troubles, yet his records were full of thankfulness. He skimmed over the bad patches, and showed expressions of deep gratitude for the blessings he enjoyed, on nearly every page. After a particularly great sorrow, he wrote: No one has had such reason as myself to say that goodness and mercy have followed me all my days. Surely the words of a happy man?

Happiness comes from the heart; doing something for someone in order to bring them happiness without any thought of reward, really does bring you happiness. But if you do it wondering all the time what you are going to get out of it, brother, you have 'had it'.

A properly balanced mind never puts self first. And a fine example is Dr Albert Schweitzer, one of the most unselfish and happiest of men. He gained fame as one of the best biographers, musician, philosopher, and theologian. He renounced everything to devote his life to helping others. He gave it all up when he became a great surgeon, that he may devote his life to bringing health and happiness to natives in the equatorial jungle. He spends his life with the lepers and is a dedicated man. And he is one of the most eminent Bible scholars in the world.

What does **he** say? 'In happiness to others you know happiness,' he says. 'Our greatest mistake as individuals is that we walk through our life with closed eyes, and do not notice our chances.'

In his hard job of complete unselfishness he has found the only true happiness, and he admits it. He urges others to do the same.

Bryan Chetwyn, a 22-year-old Liverpool boy, took up this challenge. He spent more than a year with Ethiopian lepers.

It was just over fifteen months ago that he volunteered for a year's work in a backward country with the Voluntary Service Overseas Organization.

Three days after arriving in Ethiopia, Bryan was sent 170 miles into the bush with eighty lepers, to build a village.

In the next seven months, during which he saw only one European, he directed the clearing of 144 acres of bush and helped erect workshops. Then when the village was complete, he taught the lepers to become a self-contained community.

Now, back in England, Bryan believes he has returned a wiser, more experienced, better in every way, and a happier person.

People who dedicate their lives are among the most happy. Think of Valentina, Russia's cosmonaut and first woman in space. Valentina Nikolayeva-Tereshkova, like Yuri Gagarin, the spaceman, has all the time a wonderful smile. Everybody was charmed who had the pleasure of meeting her, and she captivated viewers on their television screens. A beautiful and very happy woman.

Would she one day go back to work, adding to her forty-eight orbits of the earth, after having her baby?

Valentina married her fellow cosmonaut, Andrean. She said, 'I have promised to dedicate my life to the cosmos; the life and work of a cosmonaut.'

Wonderful, isn't it? Her great achievement brought everybody happiness. You get happiness from life if you put happiness into it. The thing you want, that you must be.

Happiness does not mean that we are to be delirious with joy every minute, nor placidly content with our lot. It is an exhilaration which comes from living life to the full, doing something for somebody else, and accepting whatever comes along in the right spirit.

Bolingbroke wrote: 'He alone is happy and he is truly so, who can say, "**Welcome life, whatever it brings! Welcome death, whatever it is!**" '

If you are feeling unhappy, the best thing you can do is to go out and find someone to help. The founder of the Boy Scouts, Lord Baden-Powell, knew this and that is why he made it a rule that every Boy Scout should do a good turn each day.

Have you seen a miserable Boy Scout? I haven't. They are happy, and never so happy as when they have knotted their kerchief, which tells the world that they have done their good deed for that day.

Many people dedicate their lives and do things to make others happy. I think of the Lady Muriel Dowding, wife of Air Chief Marshal Lord Dowding, G.S.B., G.C.V.O., C.M.G., and spearhead of the **Beauty Without Cruelty** campaign. She has dedicated her life in trying to stop all cruelty to animals, and I know of no other lady quite so dynamic in her ambition. Lord Dowding does much for the animals, too.

The Lady Muriel Dowding has always a sunny smile, obviously so happy, except when she's hearing of cruelty to animals. She is very beautiful and tireless in her devotion to the cause.

Gerald Curtler, M.A., is another whose whole life is a dedication to suffering animals. Gerald is a happy man; a smiling barrister-at-law, never so happy as when he is giving pleasure and help to other people, and to the animals he loves. Not only does he bring joy and surprise to those around him, but his every thought is to eliminate all cruelty to creatures big and small, and he is ever striving to achieve this ambition.

'A wonderful Brahmin friend emphasized to me the supreme importance of **Service before Self**,' he said. 'My most happy hours are those dedicated to others and to the weakest of the defenceless, the animals,' he adds. 'All that is best in me I have given to them, and I mean to stand by them to the last and share their fate whatever it is.'

This is Gerald's way to happiness. There are others, and it is a fine way.

Lady Blanche Robey, wife of the late Sir George, Prime Minister of Mirth, is another very happy woman. She has always the sweetest smile for you. She works unceasingly for the good of the Red Cross and other charities. She tackles her splendid work in a calm, unruffled way with a driving power which, by comparison with other people, is quite amazing. Yet she remains wonderfully happy.

There are many like these good people, who devote their lives to others and in doing so find a happiness few of us know.

Danger brings some people happiness. Danger for a cause, or danger that excites the onlooker to happiness.

Take Donald Campbell, the land and water speed ace. He is never happier than when he is speeding dangerously on the water, or along some smooth beach.

Dill-Russell, a young man of twenty-three, who was once a brilliant medical student, gave it up to devote his life to acts of illusion and escapology. He has done the most incredible things which nobody else has ever done or even attempted. They daren't. He dares anything. He is internationally famous.

Millions have been thrilled by his daring on stage and television. Wearing a strait-jacket and dangling upside down from a long rope attached to a helicopter, Dill-Russell will revolve like a Catherine Wheel, freeing himself while doing so, and throwing the jacket away.

Embedded in a box made entirely of ice, bound tight in iron bars and locked, he makes his escape. It's terrific. Lock him in any building and he will get out of it. He is the world's greatest escapologist. Danger thrills him, makes him happy, and it thrills his audiences, whether on stage or out in the open.

Dill-Russell is artistic, polished, sensitive, with immense

charm. He wants to be a millionaire, and he is psychologist enough to become one (why not?). He would very much like to meet Aristotle Onassis because he is a man who has amassed a great fortune from nothing (rags to riches) and having done it, he enjoys his life.

You may not want to dangle from a long rope attached to a helicopter, or be embedded in ice. But this is Dill-Russell's idea of happiness, and you could not meet a happier man. You would remember him always with delight because of the sunshine he radiates.

Christian Bonnington and Ian Clough made a successful ascent of the North Wall of the Eiger on August 31st, 1962. This was **their** idea of happiness and they are to be warmly congratulated.

People who live near mountains are happier than those on the plains. Why? Dr Gallup, Doctor of Philosophy of Iowa University made this discovery. He intends to find out the reason. His Gallup Poll team, who for years have been finding out what people think all over the world, are now charged with enquiring **What is happiness?**

Dr Gallup believes that if we can discover what makes people happy it may be possible to treat unhappiness clinically like a disease.

A Gallup quiz team of 50 to 100 are going out with a questionnaire which will last nearly an hour.

A girl I know told me of her happiest moment. It was when she went in a den of eight lions alone, and had a meal and champagne with them.

In the presence of nearly a thousand sensation seekers she calmly enjoyed herself. It was not until the press photographer took a picture and the flash sent them wild, that she began to wonder. But she was not disturbed. They smashed the chair and table and crockery into a thousand pieces, then calmed down. She kissed the largest and most fierce, named Pasha, and the applause was deafening. 'It was my happiest moment,' she smiled. 'Really my happiest.'

196

She was carried shoulder-high through the spectators and went home delighted that she had realized her greatest ambition.

Yes, danger has an attraction for some people. It is their way to happiness. Others delight themselves screaming at the Beatles.

There are potholers and mountaineers, those who fly aeroplanes high in the heavens, and those who go down to the bottom of the sea to find happiness amongst the coral reefs. The elephant trainer, the lion tamer, the snake charmer, all are happy in a life tinged with danger.

'What peculiar people,' you say. 'How peculiar it is to find happiness among the lepers, the lions, the excitement of escapology which even killed Houdini!' You can't figure it out. There are those who devote their lives to charitable works, to the elimination of animals' suffering, and you wonder and ask, 'Don't they ever dance? Don't they ever enjoy themselves?'

Of course they do. Like you and I. But it is the deeper things of life which bring happiness; Dr Schweitzer was right.

You repeat, 'What peculiar people.'

(Deut. 14. 2.) 'And the Lord (law) hath chosen thee to be a peculiar people.' Peculiar people are the chosen people. Chosen for what? For happiness – lasting, everlasting, happiness.

A magician knows the greatest happiness because he can perform a transformation. But before he is a true magician, able to do these wonderful things, he must know his job thoroughly and adhere to the laws.

He must have an awareness. An awareness of what he wants, of what he is going to do, of what will make him happy. And particularly an awareness of Time.

Billy Graham, that brilliantly inspired evangelist, in giving his world radio talk on the Brevity of Life, two days after President Kennedy was assassinated, said, 'Put your hand on your heart and feel it beat. It is saying, "Quick! Quick! Quick!

Only a few brief years at the most." ' And he goes on to add, 'I beg of you not to squander life.'

No one can be happy who squanders life; enjoy yourself to the very full, but give a part of yourself to other people. Do something for other people; do something to bring happiness into their lives. Like this, you will bring the magic out of your mind, and happiness will follow you like a shadow. Today, tomorrow, always.

You will not become unbalanced if you find time to meditate; you will not be numbered among the harassed, the moaning, the groaning. In this age of high-speed living, most people behave as though they had no mind.

Here is an extract from the **Dublin Evening Mail, September 9th, 1956,** with the headlines:

'He's Sensational, Stunning, and Completely Overpowering.'

And in answer to a press question:

'. . . **The hardest thing to do is read minds that are not there.'**

19
The Magic Of Romance

WHY, in a book like this, should I want to bring in romance? What has it got to do with magic?

Men and women have a mental tendency to be influenced by romance. Romance works magic and you must have the know-how about what is romantic and what is not. Before you can get the beautiful home you want, the white Jaguar, the woman of your dreams, or company of the man you most want to know, you must be able to influence someone. You must be able to attract. Men and women are behind all the things you wish to acquire, and it is important that you know how best to win them to your own way of thinking.

Romance is what everybody needs in their life, **and you must be the one who gives them a glimpse of it.** You must have a **romantic personality,** because like that, you cannot fail. Let us turn back the clock and study a romantic personality of bygone days.

Rudolph Valentino, the famous film star of the silent screen, was a very **romantic personality,** and it is undeniably true that he is impressive still, for when his films are shown today, there are massed audiences.

When Valentino was dying – when was it, thirty-seven years

ago? – following an operation for appendicitis, thousands of people hurried to the churches to pray for him.

One thousand people were on duty for his funeral.

While he lay in state for three days, admirers filed past the coffin at the rate of 150 a minute – they stopped counting after the 150,000 mark was passed.

Crowds gathered at railway stations across America as the departed star was transported from New York to Hollywood.

Rudolph Valentino was only thirty-one, an ex-gardener who became a professional dancing partner, later an actor.

The thing to remember is that Rudolph Valentino never spoke a single word in a film in his life. **He did it all with his eyes, and a personality that was romantic.** He won people who saw his silent films by sheer personality. He gave them the romantic touch which is so important, when it comes to winning all hearts.

And today we have The Beatles, a pop group – three guitarists and a drummer – who completely captivated the Queen Mother at the Royal Variety Performance, and got Princess Margaret and Lord Snowdon tapping to the tunes with their fingers. They have thousands and thousands of admirers who go miles to see them, and they writhe and shake in private ecstasy. They are said to make all who see them **supremely happy.** There are other pop groups, many quite as good, but these boys are different. Communication between the boys and their audience is an **electric** thing. There is nothing unhealthy or unpleasant about them. They make £2,000 a week, and they've hardly begun! The fans wait in the pouring rain all night long for three days to book seats a month or two ahead. People of all ages want to see them, buy their records, which are sold in hundreds of thousands. What have they got, that others lack? A **romantic personality.** And it **attracts.** It draws people in their thousands, and money in thousands!

They are refreshing. They are fun. They are kind. But above all, they are **romantic.** They attract the crowds to such an extent that the police are out in force wherever they appear. What do they communicate? Forget your worries for the moment, forget the bombs. Right now it's us, us, **us**. **Romance.**

They have **tremendous power** and the mass fervour surrounding them proves that people do need **romance** in their lives.

So determine to get this power, the unromantic get nowhere.

A young American architect proposed to his girl friend. 'I'll marry you,' she said, 'if you will sit on top of a flagpole for fifteen days.'

The boy friend had never sat on a flagpole. But he stuck it for fifteen days. When he came down his sweetheart exclaimed, 'I'm yours now!'

'Oh no, you're not,' replied the pole-squatter. 'I've had plenty of time to think up there and I've decided you're not the one for me.'

That's what she got for being unromantic! You simply can't influence anyone if your make-up isn't romantic.

Adolf Herbst, one of the eleven Mathilde miners who were entombed for fourteen days, was able to speak to his sweetheart on the surface. She comforted him with the words, 'We'll get married just as soon as you come up, darling.' He was hugged by his fiancée as he emerged from the rescue shaft and a Riviera motel owner at Cagnes-sur-Mer offered the couple a fifteen-day free honeymoon. This romantic couple attracted the attention of someone who promised them wonderful happiness.

Heinz Kull, one of the eleven trapped men, said, 'We will mark our first anniversary by taking a trip in the sun on the Mediterranean with our families.'

What could be more romantic than a trip to the sun on the Mediterranean?

The miners were to have a forty-day all-expenses-paid holiday and a shipping company offered them and their wives a free leisurely transatlantic trip aboard an ocean liner! You see how this romantic idea attracted the right people.

201

I once met an Englishman who had returned from a honeymoon abroad with his beautiful bride.

Did he talk of the Mediterranean and the magic of the moonlight? Not he.

He said, 'The place is going to be overcrowded in a couple of years. The weather was good, but of course you can't trust it. The prices are going up all the time.' And so on.

A more unromantic man I have never met. He ended his groan with, 'It's nice to get back to a glass of beer.'

I ask you? Could that man ever attract good things to him? Could he get £2,000 a week like the Beatles, or a free holiday like the miners? Never in a hundred years would that man attract a bean. He does not know the first thing about magic.

It is not until you begin to realize it, but the world is full of people who are playing their cards all wrong. I heard two women in a café talking the other afternoon. One said, 'I must get home now, dear. I have to get the ironing done before my husband gets home for his tea.'

The other woman exclaimed, 'Goodness me! Why? I never start mine until Bill gets home, then he can see what a lot of work I have to do.'

Is it any wonder that homes are broken up? The first woman had the romantic touch, everything was going to be lovely for her husband, and there was magic in her planning. The other woman, of course, would wonder why he slipped out again after tea, to post a letter or buy cigarettes; anything to get away.

There are hundreds of tragic wives whose husbands have stopped loving them, whilst others ignore romance. 'When he comes home from work he kisses me as though he had been away for months,' one woman told me. 'He follows me about from room to room. He tries to get me to sit on his lap as if we were young lovers. Sometimes I feel like screaming.'

If she really wants her husband to stop loving her, she is going exactly the right way about it. But if she loves him, she

202

needs to change her attitude quickly, and be a little more romantic.

It is remarkable how some women behave to their husbands. The first words of a famous film star, whose husband met her at the airport with a huge bouquet, were: 'Darling, **what have you been up to?**'

She greeted romance with a doubt. She spoiled a beautiful gesture with a ridiculous thought.

M. Pierre Mendes-France, French Premier and Foreign Minister, had these entries written in his London diary: ... 2 p.m. see Mr Dulles, and **Roses for Liliane**.

Liliane was his beautiful dark-haired Egyptian wife.

At 10.30 p.m. the same night, M. Mendes-France put through a telephone call from the French Embassy in London, where he was staying, to Trocadero 1430 in Paris to ask Liliane whether the roses had arrived.

The roses, in three shades of pink, were clustered in a huge basket on the drawing-room floor of the Mendes-France apartment. 'My husband never forgets anniversaries,' said Liliane, 'no matter how busy he is.' She went on, 'Once when he was away he sent me flowers, and I couldn't think why. I had to ask him. It was to mark my recovery from an operation four years before.' The Mendes-Frances are inseparable companions though they have been married well over twenty years. Romance brings the magic happiness that everybody seeks.

Shapely American showgirl Vicki Benet was thrilled one day when a knock came on her door. A page came in with a tissue-wrapped rose. She blushed. A note fell to the floor. 'To the sweetest girl in the world,' it read. Someone with a romantic personality gave the sort of pleasure that wins.

Anton Dolin, the ballet dancer, spoke of his friendship with a rich American woman thirty years his senior. It was a good friendship. Nina was eighty-four years old. She became very ill. Beside her bed there was a silver vase, and every time Anton Dolin visited her, he placed a red rose in it. Even when he was away he saw to it that she had a fresh red rose every day.

There was nothing between them but friendship, and this touch of romance made Nina very happy. It was Nina who gave him a magnificent pink and white villa in Monte Carlo that once belonged to Lily Langtry.

Another woman said, 'He always brings me roses, always the same number, always the same colour. **If only he would bring me something else, even dandelions, for a change!'**

See what I mean? You can kill romance, easily, quickly, by lack of appreciation. By not responding.

I saw a film the other day where a Spanish dancer threw a rose at a man she fancied, from a street twenty feet below, and it landed perfectly in the crook of his folded arms. You've seen that sort of thing on the films, I'm sure. Always it is a rose.

A business woman who travelled to Russia said, 'Moscow is the place where men are most romantic. My finest – and most agonizing – moment arrived when a Russian presented himself holding a long-stemmed rose. He looked at me humbly, made a brief speech of adulation, and thrust the rose firmly into the neckline of my dress – thorns and all.'

Again, it was a rose.

Evelyn Laye tells a very beautiful story. She was pinned and helmeted under the drier, when her hairdresser brought her a spray of roses.

She took the roses from him, and read the card, 'All my love, Frank.'

'Where is he?' she asked. 'He's gone,' said the hairdresser. Then he asked, 'Is it your birthday, or your wedding anniversary?'

'Neither,' she said softly. **'He just does things like this.'**

It was from Frank Lawton, her actor husband, and we all know that theirs is one of the most happy and successful marriages.

Are you a man like Mendes-France, Anton Dolin, Frank

Lawton, and many others I have not told you about? If you are not, it is worth trying to be like them, for they are **romantic personalities**, and life for them is happy, successful, and wonderful in every way. They **attract** these things.

The Spanish may throw roses, and the teenagers throw jelly babies on the stage for the Beatles, but each in their fashion are expressing romance. And wherever there is romance, there is dynamic attraction. You win that way.

To American college boys, actors and actresses in Hollywood, and elderly American millionaires, the romantic years last quite a time, because they are always falling in love, no matter what age.

Most Englishmen follow only one love affair to the end, but it can be none the less romantic.

King Solomon, who is reputed to have fallen in love a thousand times, and married a thousand women, for some reason or other was called **the wisest man on earth.** I think it is because each time he fell in love, it was a romantic affair, and romance is so important that he must be deemed a wise man.

Every city has its romance, and every village, and every heart its mad moment. Be sure you look for them. You can find romance in the charmed circle of the home. You can find romance anywhere. You must have the seeing eye to find this magic.

The Voice of Prophecy, who give such fine spiritual talks over the radio, tell the story in one of their leaflets of a unique gift that a girl's father gave to her husband on their wedding day.

It was a gold watch, and beautifully engraved upon it was the words: **Be nice to Sarah.**

Every time the young man looked at his watch, he was reminded of these words. I think it is very beautiful. The Voice of Prophecy are very realistic in their talks, and this idea seems to me to be quite romantic and lovely.

Many a woman marries a man with a small income, and

she cooks, washes and darns for him, shops and sometimes even, she goes out to work. She has not had time to look after her figure and make herself as alluring as those beautiful women they watch on TV. She has become drab and colourless, and a little irritable at times. And so she becomes less and less interested in sex and appeal, and there is no romance in her life. Yet inwardly she has the same feelings as others – she would like a romantic life, like to be admired and sought after. She must do something about it, break down the barriers, and begin to love and live. You cannot be a romantic personality if you are frustrated. These feelings of frustration will finally bring her to the doctor. She will have a nervous breakdown.

Napoleon loved his Josephine, but she was not a beauty. She had trouble with her teeth; either some were missing or they protruded, I forget which. What did she do? Every time she spoke to Napoleon, she was said to have held a beautiful lace handkerchief up in front of her mouth, and smiled with her eyes. The beautiful lace handkerchief enchanted him, and he never cared or noticed anything wrong. She is also reputed to have left dainty silk and lace lingerie thrown over the back of a chair, strewn across the bed, or dropped carelessly on the floor. But always, her magnificent pretties were on show like that. And why not? Do beautiful things have necessarily to be tucked away in a drawer forever out of sight? Any woman can do the same; can foster romance and magic in the manner of Josephine.

'Look at me, am I pretty?' said Rehna Cloete, the author, to a reporter when he called.

He examined her politely, and said cautiously, 'I think you are attractive.'

'Exactly,' she said. 'I'm not **pretty**, but I got myself a man in a thousand.'

Then she went on to say that a pretty girl might **get** herself a man more quickly, but she would not **keep** him for long unless she made herself attractive and romantic-looking.

'You've got to become expert in the glamour stuff, too,' said the author of **To Catch a Man**. 'You've got to know how to use perfume, moonlight, and your clothes to the best advantage.' She always wears gay, colourful, romantic clothes.

It's true. Wonderfully, excitingly true. And you'll know it the very first time you do these things.

Whether he's Italian, Spanish, French or English, he will say **I love you** if you are a **romantic personality**. You'll be **unforgettable**.

Any man or any woman who sets out to be a **romantic personality**, will draw the people like Rudolph Valentino and the Beatles. Nobody can stand up against it. You win all hearts.

Victor Mature, the film star, gave his girl friend, the ex-deb daughter of a surgeon, a heart-shaped locket encrusted with diamonds and rubies. On it was inscribed **I love you more than yesterday**. A touch of romance. You may not be able to afford diamonds and rubies, but a plain gold locket would work wonders engraved with those words.

This pretty love symbol can be used in many ways. Heart-shaped bouquets made with the heads of small flowers. Eight gilded hearts shining on a bracelet make a romantic gift, or a linen cloth embroidered in hearts and roses. Heart-shaped soap, heart-shaped phials of perfume, glitter hearts on a cushion, heart-shaped sachets for your nightdress or his pyjamas, heart-shaped see-through gift boxes to contain safety pins, ribbons and things for the new baby, heart-shaped patty tins for the kitchen, hearts on your apron, hearts on your girdle. There is no need for any man or woman to be without romance, while little treasures of this sort are seen here and there in a room.

Dana Wynter the actress said, 'I only met him once. He bowed and kissed my hand, and swept me back into the romantic ages.' You see little of this in our country, but on the Continent it is quite usual to see this romantic greeting. In Paris young lovers kiss in the street and nobody seems to notice. Romance is not so noticeable in this country.

And talking about kisses. A girl kisses a man, then looks at him and giggles. 'You've got lipstick all over your face.' **Romance dies a sudden death.**

Never laugh about a kiss, and never talk about them. A kiss is romantic, and romance is not a joke. It is something very magical and lovely. Something to treat with awe.

Kissing can be something very special and precious. Some of the loveliest things in life are spoilt for us by laughter at the wrong moment. Kissing is one of them. Sometimes it is given in thanks for a lovely evening; sometimes sadly because it means parting; sometimes to express an affection you can't put into words; a personal, **magic** thing.

But kiss-and-tell lips belong to the unromantic.

If one day you should visit the Taj Mahal, that beautiful love story in marble, test its peculiar echo. Stand beside the grave of those two who loved and call softly their names. From all round the building will echo the two names mingling, fainter, softer, more tenderly. Until at last, you will hear what sounds like **I love you . . . I love you.** Then it will die away and the echo is no more.

This is **romance.**

Now let me tell you about myself.

An extract from **Edinburgh Pictorial, August 6th, 1954.**

'**. . . To find out just how good Koran is off-stage we tried a little experiment on Tuesday.**

In the morning, the editor of the Edinburgh Pictorial, during an interview with the mind-reader, was asked to write any address he could think of within a radius of two miles of the Empire Theatre. He did this and the piece of paper with the address on was folded, placed in an envelope and sealed; this in turn was placed inside another envelope and sealed. No one but the editor was allowed to touch or see the piece of paper. When this operation was completed the envelope was kept in his pocket until 3 p.m. on Tuesday when the mind-reader and the editor met at the G.P.O.

The experiment was to see whether Koran, by contact

mind-reading, could find the address which had been written down. An independent witness was present during the whole experiment to verify that Koran did not have any possible chance to see or touch the paper.

Within 25 minutes of meeting Koran led the editor to the correct address. The envelope was opened and the number of the house checked by the witness. Koran had done it again!'

Then, from the Nottingham Guardian Journal, the headline – Mind-reader finds hidden address in Nottingham.

'It was fantastic – and a little frightening. I had always believed that a man's thoughts, if nothing else, were his personal property.

That was until I met Al Koran, the mind-reader, who is at the Nottingham Empire this week. Yesterday he risked his stage reputation by carrying out a strange experiment. He did it because people are sceptical of such things as mind-reading and telepathy and often label them as stunts.

So he volunteered to put his own science to a severe test. He asked a colleague of mine to write down the name and address of a friend within a two-mile radius of the city centre, and put this in an envelope. This was then sealed inside a larger envelope and handed to me when I went out to watch the experiment.

Koran had said that he would try to deliver the envelope (it might have been a romantic letter) to this address. He asked me, "Do you know where this place is?" and I replied, "Yes." "Then sit in the back of the car with me," he said.

The slip of paper inside the envelope was addressed to a friend living at 47 Hampden Street, Nottingham. "Let's make for the Midland station," Koran told the photographer who was driving. We were, of course, heading for the wrong direction, but the photographer and I sat with impassive faces.

We went down Lower Parliament Street, then along London Road. Koran did not look at all like a magician – that is, the popular conception of one. He wore a blazer and neatly

209

pressed gabardine trousers and puffed at a gold cigarette holder.

He said suddenly, "Turn right here and go up to the city centre, then past the Empire Theatre." This was certainly in the direction of Hampden Street.

On the way we chatted about all kinds of things. . . . For a moment we were heading the wrong way again, but Koran said, "Do you mind turning back, please?" He correctly navigated us to Dryden Street and there was Hampden Street, the first turning on the left.

We had just passed this turning when Koran said, "This is where we get out." I handed him the envelope and he walked confidently back down Hampden Street, went to turn into No. 37, then changed his mind.

He walked past No. 47, the house of destiny, and turned in to No. 49. Koran rubbed his chin reflectively (was this the magical touch?) and then went back to No. 47 and announced, "I'm sure this is the house, and that a young lady lives here."

It was a triumphant moment for him – and an exciting one for those who saw the experiment. How did he do it?

"By contact mind-reading," Koran told me. "You knew where to go and you led me, although you did not realize it. I picked up your mental reactions, even when you tried to put me off the scent." '

Did I say it might have been romantic? Well, there was a young lady there.

20
Health That
Brings Magic

WHY is it that there are such marked physical differences in the various classes of humanity? In some persons we see diseased and distorted figures, and in others we see fine and perfect demonstrations of radiant health? It depends so much on their thinking and eating.

Most people are only hanging on to life, they are not able to work magic. But you, as a magician, must know just how to be radiantly fit and mentally alert. As a magician you must know how best to keep fit, and how to extend your life and live a long, long time. All the magic in the world that you may work for yourself is of little value unless you are radiantly fit and able to live a long time to enjoy it. If you are beginning to make wonderful demonstrations (and you should be doing so by now) then you need glorious health to enjoy the fruits of your success.

By eating the right foods you will be able to say, 'Gone are the aches and pains, the feelings of fatigue, the deadly lassitude that kills.' You will no longer turn over in bed in the morning to sleep a while longer. You will be up with the lark, singing, glad to be alive.

You will not be touchy and irritable any more. You will never know what it is to be fagged out. This is the perfect existence. Life for you will be grand. 'The wind's on the heath, brother; who would wish to die?' That's how you will feel when you are well. Your swimming pool, your Rolls-Royce, your yacht, your palatial home, your dreams that have come true through the magic in your mind, what use are they if you are sick and tired? How can you enjoy your new-found treasures if you are old and weak?

Youth! Eternal youth! That's what you want. Bronzed and beautiful and everlasting.

Are you losing your youth? How are you losing it? And why? Left too long, youth can never be recovered. If you are not as young as you used to be when life was fun; if you are fully conscious that you are getting older, and begin to feel as one does during the last dance of a ball, tired but keen, then decide right now to **do something about it.**

You can remain young in spirit and fit in body until well over a hundred. Many people do. It is not just a matter of your attitude to life and thinking the right thoughts, but it's a matter of **what you eat.** There are foods which help enormously towards giving you the power to work magic. And there are foods which gradually numb the mind, like slow poison, so that you can never, never have that power.

Let magic play a vital and fuller part in your health plan. As a magician you have the power to bring health and beauty to the highest standard that the world has ever known, and a real tranquillity to your mind.

So let's consider food, and what we eat most of. Bread.

Bread, they say, is the staff of life. What sort of bread? Brown or white? This argument has been going on officially since Nero put the Romans on a diet of bread. Nero and his Court liked it white. Is there any difference between brown bread and white, as regards food value, sufficient that it matters?

I think so. A lady said to me the other day, 'My son and daughter have each collected some tadpoles to observe their evolution into frogs. My son put some white bread crumbs in his bowl for them to feed; my daughter put brown bread crumbs into her bowl. The next day, all my son's tadpoles were dead, but my daughter's are still thriving.'

You like white bread and you eat large quantities of it. White bread is treated to maintain its colour, but the agent used may be slowly doing to you as a white-bread eater what it rapidly did to the more fragile tadpoles. Don't you agree? Maybe it is slowly killing that 'something' in your mind that works magic. That precious 'something'. I don't say it is, but I think there is a strong possibility.

Brown wholewheat bread is the best, because the wheat germ and the outer coating of the wheat contain most of the vitamins and minerals we need, whereas white-bread millers knock out the essential ingredients to sell to other firms, or as animal feeding. They can make a little money on the side, so to speak.

Do we lose anything from our diet by eating white bread instead of brown wholewheat? 'Of course we do,' says Mr C. Donald Wilson, member of the Soil Association. 'The millers take out thirty per cent of the nutrition in wheat.' Like this, even if they put a little bit of it back, essential vitamins are lost from our diet. When you start adding chemicals to food and adulterating natural food, harm and ill-health is bound to result. Why do the Red Indians, the Africans, the Hunzas, enjoy such perfect health? Because they eat pure food grown on natural soil. To bring out the magic in your mind, you must give thought to these things.

Most people are fond of sugar. Have you considered sugar? You prefer it white. Did you know that a report from the Californian Farmer a little while ago recommends the use of sugar as a pest killer, and it quoted the scientific work to justify this:

'United States Department of Agriculture scientists have found that ordinary sugar mixed into soil acts as a highly

213

effective killer of nematodes. This is the first known nematode-killing material discovered that is non-toxic to warm-blooded animals and leaves no residue in the soil.

Sugar kills the pests. . . .'

It is only a slow poison to humans, but who wants to be killed, even slowly? It must dim the light in your mind, bit by bit, until the day comes when you are unable to think properly, and certainly you must lose all power to work magic in the end. Note the words a highly effective killer. Are you going to take a chance on it?

If you must have sugar, brown sugar that has not been messed about for whitening purposes is best, or better still, sweeten things with pure honey. Pure honey is good for you.

What about water? The Ministry of Health has now approved the addition of sodium fluoride to water. What is fluoride? Artificial or inorganic sodium fluoride is a highly toxic protoplasmic poison, thirteen times stronger than arsenic! Stronger than arsenic. You can call it rat poison, there is no difference.

Dr Gueniot of Paris, on reaching his hundredth year, declared, 'Man does not die, but he kills himself.' Little by little, you kill yourself.

Most people really don't know how good fresh, pure water can taste. The taste of ordinary water is killed with the chlorine. Well water has a clean, beautiful taste. Farm worker John Smith barred from his home officials who wanted him to use the council's water supply. He had his own well, and had been drinking it for over thirty years. The only time his wife had ever been ill was when she stayed in a friend's house. She drank the council's water and got a skin complaint.

I know people who drink rain water and are healthy. I know people who have been wracked with rheumatism, but when they started to drink only well water, the aches and pains vanished. Many country people will tell you that.

When you visualize that magnificent home you are wanting,

214

visualize a well in the garden. Don't take any chances on losing your power to work magic.

Don't just keep ticking over. Study food, and what is needed to keep you fit. Carrots and carrot juice ought always to be included in your diet. They are particularly good for the eyes and better sight. Many night-flying pilots had carrots during the war to improve their sight in the dark. Heavens alive, you want to be able to see all these lovely things you are going to get.

The onion is one of the oldest known vegetables in the world; it was among the foodstuffs which fed the Egyptian workmen who built the Pyramids.

You should eat plenty of onions, they are a purifier. Remember the Fire Walkers and how they strive all the time for purity, of mind and body.

Then there is garlic, which is so important if you want to be free of disease; if you want to keep illness at bay. Garlic was known to the Egyptians at least five thousand years ago, and garlic is mentioned in an Indian Sanskrit treatise of Salerno eight hundred years ago.

Garlic is a powerful natural cleansing medium. During the plague of London a man walked through the streets calling 'Bring out your dead,' and he escaped the disease by rolling a bulb of garlic continually in his mouth. Serve it at main meals during serious epidemics. During the plague of London whole households were saved from the scourge by the good offices of the garlic. Likewise it is said that grated ginger is considered of equal value. Many people sprinkle it on top of stout for the great benefit it is to health.

Of all the herbs that grow, parsley is one of the most precious. More than 12,000 tons of parsley are produced in Britain each year, but only a small percentage is eaten. Parsley contains four times as much Vitamin C as an equal weight of oranges. It has more iron, calcium, and phosphorus than most fruits and vegetables. The Roman charioteers included an abundance of parsley in their horses' diet. Not

215

only did it provide stamina but made the horses fleet-footed. It has been considered more precious than laurel – a symbol of honour and glory. Entrants for the Isthmian Games were fed on parsley and the winners crowned with parsley garlands. A few years ago 'Miss Herb' was crowned in Poland with a garland of parsley after winning a beauty contest.

Sprigs of parsley are eaten at religious festivals for **purification** purposes. Purification again. You mustn't lose sight of that. We are aiming at **purity** all the time. The more **pure** you are in mind and body, the easier is it for you to reach the highest dimensions and so work magic of a spectacular kind. Eat a raw onion every day, if only a very small one, and eat as much parsley as you can every day, raw, chopped fine. There is great value in these two things. The purer your food is the more sensitive you will become. And that is important if you want to be a magician. You must be **sensitive**.

Coconuts are something you knock down at fairs; hardly ever do you go into a shop and buy one. Did you know that if you were stranded on a desert island with nothing to eat or drink but coconuts, you could go on living and be well, indefinitely? The milk of the coconut has immense value; also the nut, of course. Herman Brinkman of Kassel, Hessen, lived entirely on coconuts for a very long period. When he spent four months in Zanzibar and Kenya, he existed solely on the coconut for food and drink, and he never contracted a tropical disease, nor was he ever in need of a doctor. The coconut is one of the finest things to eat and drink. Even if it means a revolution in your diet, do include these things that make for long life and radiant health. One could mention endless fruits and vegetables which are a 'must' and which you should take daily; blackcurrants, oranges, apples, the banana (which has everything), and good cheese. Study the subject of right foods and apply them in your diet. To bring out the magic in your mind, you must be above-average health.

What gives a gorilla its enormous strength? Nuts. Just

plain nuts. Dates are a simply wonderful pick-me-up when you are tired. Oh yes, I could go on and on, but I want you to study these things yourself. All I say is that right diet is a necessary part of your programme, if you want to have the right mind and body for working magic, and for gaining youth so that you can enjoy your material treasures for a long, long while.

You need not be a **vegetarian** to work magic, but not eating meat helps you more to acquire that **purity** you are after. The longer I live the more convinced I am that the state of health of millions of men and women is only a shadow of what it ought to be.

The world's best-known vegetarian was perhaps the famous thinker and playwright, the late George Bernard Shaw. He was told by his doctors that he would die unless he ate meat. What did he do? He replied, without any fear in his heart: **'Well, let us try the experiment. Only, if I succeed, I shall expect you all to become vegetarians.'**

He survived to a good old age. He wrote: **'My situation is a solemn one. Life is offered to me on condition of eating beef-steaks, but death is better than cannibalism. . . .'** He was renowned for his fine physique, and told us that he always finished his lunch with an apple or orange. The Tibetan yogis and Indian fakirs, who can do the most magical things, on a vegetarian diet, make you wonder why we are so keen on meat.

Dr Allen E. Bannik found the secrets of long life in this fabulous country. One of the secrets is that for 2,000 years they have lived in complete isolation. They are in the world but not of it. When the doctor returned home he started to grow his own food in the organic way that the Hunzas taught him. There is mineral strength in their food which makes them germ-resistant. We could benefit in the same way if we gave up all this mad fertilizer business and poison sprays and the rest of it. No disease has ever gained a hold in their country. Vegetables and fruit are grown in organic manures

217

without artificial fertilizers. Their strength is incredible. It is a known fact that men of eighty can walk sixty-five miles and back, then return to their work immediately. And they walk erect.

They eat apricots, stone and all. The stone, they say, is the best part. The oil in the stone gives richness to the blood. They eat a lot of fresh and dried fruit, and nuts. They rise at five in the morning and go to bed early.

And don't forget the **isolation**. That is why meditation is so good for you – you isolate yourself completely, and **think**.

Yehudi Menuhin, the great violinist, believes so much in organic food that he has opened a food shop in London where only organic food is served. Yehudi is handsome and upright, and has a very fine mind. Stamina wins my admiration. With his fellow members of the Organic Food Society, he sells 'food of unspoiled flavour and goodness produced under natural conditions'.

Are we all being slowly poisoned by chemical preservatives and sprays? Dr Frank Bicknell, a British food expert, believes we are.

Yehudi Menuhin believes we are. And I believe we are. I believe that unless your food is right, you cannot be alert in your mind and fit in your body. To live long and enjoy the fruits of your demonstrations you should consider what you eat, and take only those things which make for a healthy long life.

When Charlie Chaplin recently fathered his eleventh child at seventy, the world tittered and marvelled.

Charlie has the stamina and energy of a man half his years. He swims and plays tennis, for exercise. But most of all, he eats only the right foods. Dr Robert R. Gross, an internationally famous nutrition expert, declared recently that Chaplin has stuck to a diet which is one of the healthiest the doctor has ever known. It includes plenty of fruit, a daily salad of lettuce, celery, sweet red peppers, cucumbers, parsley, carrots and tomatoes, plus a baked potato, rice, lentils, soya beans and natural cheese.

Dr Gross says that such food helps to retain vitality well into old age.

David Niven, the famous film star, gets headlines like **Time stops for the ageless Niven.** He is said to look younger every time you meet him, despite the fact that 1964 will be his thirtieth year as a film star. He is one of the richest and most powerful men in Hollywood. He is all for **organic** foods in their natural state. He is so youthful that everyone turns to look at him. Man ages and kills himself through abuse, malnutrition, and that deadly creeping poison. As a magician, you should know which are the right foods, and determine to be ever young.

I would like to see you with a library of books on right foods for health, and have you read them until they were a very part of you. It is no good doing it by halves. **All your food must be right.**

Women who refuse to grow old are many, among them, as we all know, the beautiful Marlene Dietrich. Vivien Leigh is another. They look many years younger than they are, and have endless vitality and charm.

Did you know that the ancient Greeks lived two hundred years or more apiece? Vigorous to the last and no grey hairs. Justin Glass tells about all this in a paperback, and reminds us that Thomas Park lived in London for 207 years! When you begin to study age and read all the books you can on the subject, you will find that there are an endless number of cases (all true) where people have lived well over a hundred.

Does one have to be a vegetarian to acquire this wonderful health and long life?

Does being a vegetarian help as regards working magic?

It helps a lot, because it clears your mind and purifies your body. It helps you to think, and particularly to listen in to your subconscious. It takes away all heaviness and lightens your step.

It is not a necessity, but an advantage. You become more sensitive, feel more deeply, and more gentle. Heavy meat eaters are apt to be aggressive at times, more easily disturbed, prone to bad tempers.

Many of the world's strongest men are vegetarians, and certainly the strongest animals are. The gorilla eats nuts, the horse does not eat meat, neither does the elephant. If you eat meat for strength, you are making a big mistake.

Johnny Weissmuller, the screen Tarzan, never ate meat. George Arliss, the famous film star of the old days, was a vegetarian. Today, Rupert Davis, better known as **Inspector Maigret**, is a strict vegetarian. He eats all the right foods, which include garlic, plenty of parsley, salads, and herb omelettes.

You may think a meal without meat is dull. I know a lady who dined at the home of the Lady Dowding and her husband, Air Chief Marshal Lord Dowding. They are strict vegetarians, and she has never stopped talking about that meal. 'It was the very nicest I've ever had,' she says. 'I shall never forget it.' The Lady Dowding, of course, is spearhead of the **Beauty without Cruelty** campaign and does wonderful work. Can she perform magic? At one time she had a lot of mice in her house. She said to them, **I love you very much, but please go away.** They went, every one of them, quickly. I have known people to talk to their wasps like this. The Lady Dowding certainly has magic in her voice; she speaks softly, sincerely, with love. I think it was a wonderful demonstration of the power of the spoken word.

It takes more than food to be healthy. I am thinking of baths, more baths, and still more baths. Baths of olive-oil, baths of salt, sea-water baths, baths of milk and wine, and many other luxurious washings so essential to longevity and physical well-being.

Baths have been used as aids to youth and beauty for thousands of years, and both the Romans and Greeks, when Rome and Greece were in the zenith of their glory, were firm patrons of the bath as a means to physical fitness and good looks.

Did you know that there were eight hundred and fifty public baths in ancient Rome? More than eight hundred baths in one city! Think of it. The Romans and Greeks indulged in luxurious bathing far more than we do, and they were a very beautiful race of people.

Soap and water is not enough. A Roman bath had several stages; it began with a cold one, which was followed by a tepid, and then a hot one, after which the bather was frictioned and massaged, and finally anointed with oils.

In olden days, also, the beauties of the court of France vied with each other in inventing new baths for the beautification of the skin.

A daily bath may be counted as one of the first essentials to long life and rejuvenation. It is perfectly true, tried, and tested. An experience is related of how Sir William Arbuthnot Lane went to the Rockefeller Institute and was shown by Dr Abers Carrel the first living tissues he had been able to grow on a microscope slide. It was discovered that if he fed these pieces of tissue once a day **and washed them out once a day,** they grew and thrived. If he fed them once a day **but did not wash them for two days,** they grew feeble **and died.**

Through lack of a daily bath, decay and death set in immediately. 'This proved,' said the doctor, 'that the tissues would grow indefinitely if fed **and washed.**' It makes you think, doesn't it?

The human body is a vast group of tiny living cells. All of the cells, all over the body, must be **constantly bathed every day.** I could go on and on at great length, but I think I have said enough to make you realize the importance of a bath. I want you to be able to work magic. I have written all these pages trying to show you the way, and I don't want you to fail in your demonstrations because of not doing the things you should.

Another secret of longevity is massage from head to foot every morning and evening. It is one of the quickest methods of increasing and maintaining youthful buoyancy. After a fall, our first instinct is to rub ourselves. This is because it is the natural thing to do. Nature intended us to rub ourselves.

You cannot massage yourself with your clothes on. You have to strip if you would do it properly.

Once you feel the exhilaration of massage, you never want to leave it off. That is as it should be. You are working for a fit mind and body, in order that you can bring out the hidden magic, and massage is one of the things that you should always do. It gives you life and fitness, so that you are able to enjoy your successes to the full. So that you are a good example to others. So that people admire you and believe in you. So that you attract.

Massage unlocks the door to radiant health, strength, and long life. Massage makes you efficient.

It possesses the unique feature of co-ordinating the action of all the vital organs, muscles, and other parts of your body, which are strengthened simultaneously. If loyally and steadfastly followed, it rewards the performer with superb health and vibrant energy. The passing years will seem to leave you untouched physically, if you strip daily (you can do this in your bathroom) and massage yourself all over.

You can start at first by sprinkling talc on your palm and 'polishing' your skin with your hands. To do this all over is most rejuvenating, and encourages the flow of a natural lubricant, making the skin soft and velvety. When you have thoroughly accustomed yourself to this practice, you may like to use oil, and as you become more spartan and used to the sun and air on your nude body, you may go one further, and submit yourself to an ice massage.

There have been wonderful cures from massage; the strong fingers with the gentle strength of the masseur brings healing with the touch. Take the case of a nine-year-old boy, Cecil. Cecil was rapidly losing the use of his legs when he was brought for cure by massage. Then the boy became stronger every day, and soon the time came when he could romp and play and kick a ball about.

An old lady with a fractured leg, so stiff that she could not move it, took massage, and now waves her stick in the air.

A youth in an invalid chair, wearing a spinal jacket which the doctors said he would never be able to take off, had a few weeks' treatment, and has not only thrown off his jacket, but rides a bicycle to and from a job he found for himself.

Massage on the bare flesh has, and can, straighten distorted limbs, release strictured nerves, and restore circulation. Massage helps the vital spark of repair which is in every human body. Nature does the rest.

Massage dispels all nerves and gives you an Olympian calmness and poise. Massage searches out every cell and sinew, rousing them and tuning them into harmony. Massage makes your body sing.

There are no short cuts to health. It must be acquired and maintained throughout life by the observance of strict rules, massage and right diet.

Another thing which is splendid for your strength is to treat yourself to bags of sea salt. It is quite cheap. Use it to the point of wickedness. Be extravagant. Many acrobats who amaze the public by holding a person up on one hand (for quite a length of time) and similar feats, daily rub salt water on the arms to build strong muscles. Table salt will do.

And dancing is very good for you. Everyone who values his health should dance, because dancing teaches all sorts of really important things so necessary to radiant health, such as balance, rhythm, harmony of brain and movement, and self-control. Dancing awakens in you the desire to do beautiful things beautifully, and brings wonderful tranquillity to the mind. All magicians do the beautiful things of magic, beautifully. The Magical Claudine has beautiful grace of movement as she goes from one magical turn to another. Her hand gestures are a poem. But she is not the only one. You will find that all magicians have tremendous style in putting things over. Nothing is done clumsily. There is grace worth watching and studying. Dancing gives you this grace. And you, as a magician, must master it.

Here is the story of a famous dancer. Once a puny boy of seven, 'Red' McCarthy started with fear when anyone spoke to him. Every few seconds a leg would twitch violently, and he would twist his neck and writhe. His condition had got so bad that he had to be sent home from school.

This boy, who suffered from the worst form of St Vitus' Dance, was to become a famous Olympic athlete and a great and lovely dancer, dancing nude but for the scantiest sequin loin-cloth. (Getting the air to his body.)

Dancing fascinated him, and at the end of twelve months he was really brilliant, and what was more important, every trace of his terrible malady had vanished. Rhythm, fresh air, and giving his body all the sunshine he could, had done what no doctors could do.

This 'hopeless' invalid became 'Red' McCarthy, the **Silver Phantom** dancer on skates. At the World Fair, Chicago, he amazed thousands by his spectacular barrel-jumping act. Leaping over as many as fifteen nineteen-inch barrels, he would jump twelve, twisting in the air so that he landed backwards on one foot, a feat never attempted by anyone else. He made 24,862 of these jumps. Dancing completely cured his ills and his nerves and will do the same for you, or anyone who takes up dancing for health.

Everything in life is rhythmical, as wave upon wave on the seashore, day follows night, the four seasons follow one another in due succession. You should cultivate rhythm; rhythm in the open air and sunshine particularly. It is the finest way to youth, the finest way to vitality and radiant health. Skipping is also a splendid way to keep fit.

As you proceed, step by step, practising right diet, and massage, dancing, skipping, and all the many things necessary to your health, you will notice changes taking place in yourself. Your mind will be more alert, your whole outlook on life will become more positive, and you will begin to live as you were meant to live. You will be able to do what you want at any time, never mind the difficulties. All barriers will be down, you will be able to bring out the magic in your mind because, most important of all, these things will make you positive, magnetic, able to achieve mind-control. You will wonder why you never did these things before.

An extract from **Fitness magazine, October 1958.**

'. . . **Indeed, he is as great a psychologist as he is a magician, and has lectured at Cambridge University and before many distinguished audiences. In its relation to physical health, he believes that fitness of the mind plays an all-important part.**

Al Koran says . . . "We are free men; free to eat what we fancy, or to eat intelligently and cultivate a healthier taste; free to climb to the stars, and free to slide down into our own particular hell." '

21
The Magic
Of Time

EVERYBODY should know how to make time for magic. I know there are other things to think about, like shopping, parties, motoring trips, the cinema, a theatre show, dinner with the Joneses, exercises to keep fit, books to read, the garden to be dug, the attic to clear out, and never a minute to call your own. But every magician needs time, and to achieve magic in this life, you must **make** time. You must make time for meditation every day, that is certain. You must make time to speak to your subconscious. You must make time to listen. And you must make time to look at the pictures you have pasted in your book of the things you want. And you must make time to read these words I am writing, over and over and over again, until they become a very real part of you.

Oh yes, you can always **make** time to do the thing you want to do, if you want it enough. You can make time for meditation if you are determined to work magic. You can make time to go to your private 'retreat' now and again. You can make time to turn over the pages of your scrap book, if you want the things enough, and by the power of visualization you can make by comparison the transformation of Cinderella's pumpkin into a glass carriage – child's play.

Time! There has never been enough of it. The sad little phrase of our age is, 'I haven't had time to think.'

Time is the most magical thing. You must make it somehow.

Once at Mr So-and-so's house I discovered in the bathroom a chart on which were printed horizontally the days of the week: Monday, Tuesday, Wednesday, and so on, and under each day was listed every single article of clothing Mr So-and-so was going to put on that day.

It was Monday. A glance at the chart and I knew I should see Mr So-and-so the next morning wearing a blue double-breasted suit, blue and white striped tie, grey socks with red clox, black oxfords, grey top coat flung carelessly over his arm. Carelessly!

'Until I devised this chart,' he said to me, 'I wasted **five whole minutes** in my bath each morning deciding what suit to wear.' He paused and fixed the eye of success upon me. 'I advise you to put **that** in your book. **Five whole minutes!** Tell them to do the same.'

I know many men and women who are convinced that to look smart and to change your clothes frequently is a sure way to prosperity. Never to wear the same clothes twice to the meeting or party you last went to. And these people keep a similar chart on the inside of their wardrobe door. Sounds silly, perhaps, but little things like this save five minutes here and five minutes there, and in the day could save an hour!

Yes, it may sound idiotic, far-fetched, and stupid to you. It may even sound vain. But it is one of the things tycoons and successful people do in order to **make time.**

When you are a busy person with loads of work to get through and a lot of calls to make, you **organize** time. You have to do all manner of strange things to **make** time, in order to save minutes which, over a day, a week, a month, and a year can amount to hours and hours saved.

'Ah,' you say, 'I haven't all those clothes.'

No, but you will have, won't you, when you know how to bring the magic out of your mind? And you can apply this system to other things, even the chores.

I know a successful hostess who keeps a book specially for writing down the menu she prepares for her guests the last time they came to dinner. What they like and what they don't like. When she is entertaining she does not **waste time** wondering what to get or if they will like it, or if she is repeating what they had before. She has become a hostess with time on her hands.

How quickly the time passes. It is a feeling which assails us all. Time! There has never been enough of it. The sad little phrase of our age is, 'I haven't had time to **think**.'

There does not seem time to do half the things you want to do. The day is gone. You have no time. Why? **Time is the most magical thing.** You must get it somehow. **You must make it.**

Hazlitt says: 'Like a clown at a fair, we are full of amazement and rapture, and have no thoughts of going home, or that it will soon be night.'

'Ah, make the most of what we yet may spend,' sang the ancient Persian poet and philosopher. Omar's philosophy must be **your** philosophy. Go out for the day. The day will seem much, much longer, getting away from the sameness; the routine. It will lengthen your day. Give yourself plenty of days' outings; life will be longer, or seem longer to you. It's being glued to one spot, doing the same thing day after day, that makes time go so quickly. Sameness kills. That way madness lies. Many a tycoon takes the day off to go away somewhere and have a quiet reflection on the problems of being alive.

'But I can't spare the time,' you say. How often I have heard that. Yet time must be found for healthy relaxation, for learning to do magic, for thinking. Making time for these things is absolutely essential. Your days may be one long rush, hustle and bustle from dawn till dark, but it doesn't get you there in the end. It doesn't bring you magic, it brings you a nervous breakdown.

Just as it takes a pianist a long time to become a Paderewski and there must be long training before one can breed pedigree dogs or race horses, so must there be long training if you want to become a perfect and clever magician. You have to make sacrifices in order to make the time required.

What most of us want is a plan for more time to get well; a plan which will put new life and vigour into our backbone, a flash in our eye, a spring in our step.

You should have a programme for this and a chart for that, so that not a moment is wasted. You must have a sufficiency of fresh air and deep breathing, the two things so necessary if you would be strong and fit, in a physical state to work magic. You cannot bring magic out of a sick mind. You have to be well first. A sick person can help themselves get better by right thinking, but you must be fit if it's magic you want.

Others may fall around you like leaves or be mowed down like flowers by the scythe of Time, but it is not until you see the best of your health fading, and your own pleasures and power cut up by the roots, that you really begin to think.

You should commence, first of all, by going carefully through your usual day's programme, to see what time is wasted. Everybody wastes time, except the few who are time-conscious. There are things you have been meaning to do for years. A language to learn, a dress to make, promotion to earn, music to improve, that alteration in the attic, the top room to be done out, the garden. . . .

That game of bridge with the Smiths each week. Why not make it a fortnightly meeting? You can save an evening there. The minutes you save can be put to good purpose, the purpose of attaining a powerful, positive mind.

You may even be able to cut out a meal once a week, by having high tea, or late dinner only and skipping the tea.

The half-hour or so you save on one meal instead of two can be much better used recharging your battery.

No time is a weak-kneed excuse. You must know how to control time, how to leave time each day for the exhilarating practice of deep breathing. You must not be Time's fool. There beyond those curtains lies the garden, a beautiful place for fresh air and quiet in the very early morning, but you hardly ever see it. At least not at that time. You turn over on the other side and go to sleep again! There has been no time for anything, anything but playing football or filling in your pools.

Make an effort to rise earlier, and once having mastered that ordeal, you can spare some time before breakfast to do some of the things you have long wanted to do.

There is nothing worse than to keep on chanting, 'I must do so-and-so, I must do . . . I must . . . I must. . . .'

'One day I must . . .'; then follows the famous alibi, 'but I never seem to have **time**.'

Life is to **act**, and not to do is death. There must be action, and you must **act now**. The clock is ticking its way towards eternity and your end, so why go on tired and worn out – a failure?

It is not how long you have lived that matters, or how much longer you are going to live, **but whether you are alive at all!**

Why not commence this very day to grow stronger and more radiantly happy, by making time for magic? There is a difference between mere existence and **life**.

I know a lot of people who are 'going to' get married when they have the time. They are 'going to' write a letter, 'going to' sing a song, 'going to' say a prayer, 'going to' travel, 'going to' this and that, **when they have the time!** It is the farthest they will ever get, because every day the opportunity comes to them.

There are people belonging to a certain school who walk around the room on the tip of their toes, describing a circle in the air with their hands as they say: 'I am going to travel right round the world.' They make the circle with their arms, 'I am going to travel right round the world.' It is a health school, and it sounds mad, but at least it impresses the idea upon their minds, and they get elevated and the desire grows.

Magic has caused me to travel a good way round the world, and I would like you to do the same. It is a wonderful experience, and if you haven't been, you don't know what you are missing. The very thought of it makes for a healthy mind. No wonder they teach them that way in the school I was telling you about.

You can achieve astounding success, if you determine to **make time.** Leave that game of golf with Bill next Saturday, or that house-warming party with the Joneses on Monday. Snap your fingers at a few things like this, and make the time for magic and success.

And get the wanderlust into your blood. Do a trip to the nearest seaside resort (on your day off) and never mind the weather, or go to the hills. Start simply like that. If you cultivate the wanderlust, bigger ventures will follow. But make a move by going somewhere.

Think of it! The ticket. The train. The packing of a suit-case, the slamming of a door, the escape from that eternal sameness of every day. What excitement to be able to say, 'I shall be going away next week.' What a thrill, even if it is only a little journey, it will mean much to you. I travel a lot, so I know.

It is the prelude, that's the thing. Making a start; making time. It is the stepping stone to foreign travel. Let the hang-over go hang, and beat it! Beat it to the place you want to go to. And when you have got travel into your blood and under your skin, when it has become a part of you, be sure that through the **law of attraction** you will draw to you the ways and means for that bigger, better, round-the-world adventure.

Now is the appointed time. Never, in any age, have people

231

had such marvellous chances to see the world as they have today, to get out of the rut into an aeroplane, a streamlined train with its buffet car, or a luxurious motor coach, unheard of in the past. And when you have learned magic, you will be going in your own beautiful car.

Go and see wonderful places.

'I was happy then, although I did not realize it at the time.' How often have I heard that said, oh, dozens of times. People look back, and sometimes they look forward, but seldom ever do they look at the present moment. Develop an awareness of everything that goes on in and around you – the given moment.

'I'll do it tomorrow' is the attitude, and it is wrong. People who achieve things in life **discipline their time.** Nothing is wasted. They make good use of every moment. Others decide to do a thing **now,** but go and watch television or play tennis instead. Do the thing you have always wanted to do **now,** or make your plans **now,** or speak to your subconscious about it **now,** not tomorrow. You will get a feeling of expectancy. Let your feet dance, and not drag yourself wearily along life's cobble-stones. Like produces like. If you are elated with the thought of good things coming soon, in time for you to enjoy them, you will want to dance your way through life today and every day, and like this you attune yourself to the right vibration. You will set in motion the magnetic power that will bring you your wildest dreams. But **now** is the time to feel the expectancy, not tomorrow, or next week. Sometimes the reaction to your joy and expectancy results in immediate magic, as though things materialize overnight, so to speak. If there is no joy or deep feeling in your life at the moment, the time is wrong to look for a demonstration. Feeling is so very important; the feeling of the moment – not how you felt yesterday or how you are going to feel tomorrow.

To make time work magic, you must speed up your feelings. You must be enthusiastic and happy **now.** You will never have any more time than you have today. It is how you use your twenty-four hours that counts. You want your car quickly, your house quickly, and the more excited you are at the thought of it, the speedier will it come to you.

The Hon. Angus Ogilvy, who married lovely Princess Alexandra, has often made do with three hours' sleep only, at night. It is said that he thinks sleeping is more or less a waste of **time**. Often he has done without any sleep at all when he has had a particular busy social and business pro-gramme.

But he is a great believer in **solitude**, particularly in Scotland, where great solitude and great beauty go hand in hand. This busy and most successful personality finds time – **makes time** – for solitude and thinking. You have to do that. You **have** to make the time. All fine characters become fine through solitude.

Don't be put off with the thought that you haven't the time. If you have no time to develop the various things which go towards bringing the magic out of your mind, you have a leakage somewhere of the precious minutes that make up your day. You are frittering time away, and not using it for development. Don't waste any more time brooding over the past and what might have been. Don't waste any more time being fearful of the future. **Live a day at a time,** and use those twenty-four hours wisely.

Look cheerfully on each new day, confident that it will be well worth living. With Carlyle you will be able to say: 'Waste not time – here is a whole Earth and a whole Heaven, and we have eyes to look on them.'

The proper use of time means having a sense of direction. This is where your subconscious mind can be so helpful. You can go into the silence and ask for right direction, and if you listen carefully, you will get it, and you will know that it is right.

You cannot be really happy if you have no time. Nothing is so tiring as the obsession, 'I must . . .' Budget your time. Determine that it shall not master you.

Here is the attitude a certain author took when writing a

233

best-seller. He told himself that life would be really grand for him if, at the end of five months, he had most of the things his heart craved for.

So he planned and schemed to get them. It would take him five months to write the book. He planned to be alive, yet dead as it seemed, to everything and everybody, for one hundred and fifty-three days! How tremendously strange it would seem, but not impossible.

Balzac did it. Why shouldn't he? The author of **La Vie Prodigieuse** locked himself in his room with his manuscripts and a coffee-pot for days and days and, at the end, his room looked like a battlefield! But he attained.

Conrad did the same thing. He locked himself in his study away from the outside world, and he stayed there until he achieved what he set out to do. When he had finished his book, he rightly called it **Victory**.

Does it matter how hard the tasks you set yourself or how varied, if you know that five months will see you through? One hundred and fifty-three days! 'Well,' said the author, 'if I were dead, people would have to get used to not seeing me; not talking and laughing with me again. They would soon get used to it.'

Five months! No more incessant chattering in cafés and public-houses. No more silly knocks upon the door to ask if I wanted a vacuum cleaner, a scribbling pad, and if not, why not? He said to himself, 'I shall not be at home any more to anyone.' No more invitations to lunch, to tea and that billiards match, to cocktails, to dinner. No more dancing to gay music under romantic shaded lights, no more golf. No more wondering what clothes I shall put on today, or when I would like my bath.

He told himself that nothing like this would matter any more. These one hundred and fifty-three days of his five months' plan to write a best-seller would be his very own. He would be free. No use anyone wanting to come and look at the curtain rods. No one daring to ask what he wanted for lunch. He would be able to say to himself: 'Nobody can ring me up, for I do not exist any more to anybody.' Cars would come and cars would go, but none of them would bear friends to his flat. He was going to be 'out'. He was going to cut himself off entirely from civilization, and achieve! Time and silence and peace would belong to him, and in them he would build, build, **build**.

And it is the same with men and women. They grow rich and successful, not in the rush and hustle of life as it is today, but in the dark and quiet interludes, whether the interludes be five years or five months, or five minutes.

The author with this idea smiled at the thought that after breakfast he would be able to lounge in his dressing-gown with a cigarette and smile and smile at nothing. Nobody could call him an idiot. They would not be there to see him. And on the last day of his five months' plan the world would be his oyster. His book, as you will have guessed, achieved **fantastic sales**. He had **made time**. Where there's a will, there's a way. You too can **make time**. I have done this sort of thing for short periods when I have wanted to do some particular magic that needed thought and solitude.

We say we will keep this or that engagement, if we have time. We will do this thing or that thing, if we can manage it. Yet we **can** keep the appointment, **can** do the job. And we know it.

How often do you hear people say they have been 'Too busy to write,' that they have 'no time for friendship'? Can't be bothered to visit, to telephone, to say thank you on a postcard, to congratulate. No time . . . too tired . . . too busy . . . can't be bothered. . . .

But are they so much more busy than other people? I think not.

And there are those who **waste** time. There are people who actually go to bed at half-past nine every night because, they complain, there is nothing else to do.

In one of his books, J. B. Priestley emphasizes the folly of it. His heroine compares London with her gloomy Midland town, and she says:

'. . . where I live everybody always wants to go home. . . . We're frightened of going home to bed. We set out to make an evening of it, hoping to meet on the way the immortal realities – love, friendship, laughter, beauty, wisdom. If not one of them turns up, we stay on and on, in the hope that they will. **To go home to bed is to acknowledge defeat.'**

This is perfectly true. If one goes to bed because one thinks there is nothing else to do, one is a complete failure. You turn your back on magic. Everywhere you come up against people who are turning their backs upon magic. They drink, play bridge, dance to the radio, shuffle the cards again, knit, in fact anything for the sake of something to do; anything to **kill time,** the stuff that life is made of!

Never **kill** time. This is fatal to magic. Demand that every minute may mean something wonderful to you and yours. Life at its longest is but 'Hail, and Farewell'. Let the Hail be hearty, and the Farewell without regrets.

Nancy Jay wrote a good story that gives you a strong sense of time. It was of a young man and girl, very much in love. But the young man did not want to marry just yet. **There was plenty of time.** It was not that Micky could not afford to marry. It was not that he did not love her. 'We're plenty young,' he said.

Then something happened. It was that night when he said, 'I'm coming in to say good night.'

'You'll have to go through the shop,' Mary said.

She was going to turn on the light, but 'Who wants light?' he said.

Then, as they were saying good night in each other's arms, the light in a neighbour's window was turned on, and Micky started suddenly.

He saw, standing one above the other, some tall, some short, all poignant with their unmistakable shape – rows of finished and unfinished coffins. . . .

'Mary,' he said, 'you've got to marry me very soon.'

I like that story. It's so natural, and it brought home to Micky the sense of time.

'Another day gone, and nothing done yet. Soon all the days will be gone, and nothing ever will be done.'

You have lived, you have eaten, drank, loved, bathed, suffered, talked, danced in the night and rejoiced in the dawn, but still you are behindhand with time.

The day is gone. You long fiercely to return to yesterday. You would behave differently. You would not waste a single moment. Suddenly you are conscious of intense life hurrying swiftly to an end. The clock is ticking its way towards eternity. You cannot get back what has gone.

Panic seizes you.

You are always **going to** enjoy tomorrow, next week, next year – never today.

This little extract from Reyner Barton's short story **He was Time's Fool** is reminiscent of nearly everybody today:

'Suddenly Scalson realized his bondage, and saw for the first time the ropes that had bound him.

'Yet he had made a success of things; no one would deny that. He would leave a hundred thousand behind him when he went. . . . Yes, he'd made plenty of money; and how had he made it? Through seeing his watch kept right time, and that he himself kept right time with his watch. . . .

'Scalson raised his head and looked about him. All those books that there had been no time to read! What was there inside them, what had he missed? There, beyond those closed curtains, lay his garden; a beautiful place, and he hardly ever saw it. **There was no time,** no time for anything but the tasks he had set himself to fulfil.

'Time had taken his life **and had worked it to death.**

'Mr Scalson stood up with a jerk. **To death?** . . .'

And so the story goes on. You can work yourself to death and never know the magic that is happening every day around you. We all know the wife who says, 'John, why won't you be like other husbands? It's always work, work, work! Don't I count for anything in your life?'

And we all know the husband who answers back, 'My dear, when I make my pile we'll take a cruise around the world.'

'Some day when I make my pile. . . .' But 'some day' never comes. Our motto has been **'Leave it.'**

You pretend that if only conditions were different you would live. You would have fun. But you do not make the effort to alter the conditions. You say with the crowd, you are **going to** and you get nowhere and see nothing.

You have not had time to look at the moon, to dress for dinner, to do a show, to write 'bless you' on a card and send it to a friend. You have been too busy trying to make a pile. Yet by a little daily meditation you can learn magic, and get your pile without having to make a slave of yourself. Without having to work hard.

Is the word **fun** foreign to you? Have you acquired a warped conscience which makes you guilty unless you work as hard as your grandparents?

This is fatal to happiness. This is wrong. Dozens of new discoveries have been made since our grandparents' day and now there is no need to slave incessantly from morning till night, week in and week out, with no bright spots, no romance, no adventure. We are living in the air age, the age where mind is being recognized for what it is. When you are able to work magic, and get all the things you want through the power of your mind, you will not need to slave. They will come to you without slavery. What you have got to do is get your mind right; get the right attitude.

You must organize your life so that there is time for magic, so that you have energy to **live** as well as earn a living. Again I repeat, **you must make time.** You must change the **you** that existed before you picked up this book. There must be a **new you** to correspond with what it takes to work magic.

238

It's no use saying you will start in the spring, and then get on with your work in the same old way, slogging along with the idea that in the spring you will change, study, and become the magician I want you to become. No, the time for action is **now**. Visualize yourself as a person who always does things **now**. Make up your mind to be that sort of a person, then you will find that you never waste a moment, because there is no delayed action. Everything you want to do, you do **now**. Or at least make the plans for it now. You will feel a warm glow around your heart, when you take that attitude. Create a new life pattern. Remember what you have already learned about magic, and **find time** to continue to master the whole secret. Making time for the study of magic is absolutely essential, if you would be radiantly fit and strong, happy, wealthy, and **alive**. It takes **time** to become a magician. Lots of time. You must reflect. You must reflect upon the problem of getting time for magic, upon the happiness and success you will get from it, upon the direction you are going, and what life is giving you. The less you reflect, the less chance you have of ever becoming a magician.

Magic is **not** for you? Too difficult, too much to do? It **is** for you, I passionately repeat, **'It is for you.'** Throw away the idea, and you throw away the most precious suggestion that was ever offered to you. **Make** time, and try it!

People get in a rut, they are afraid to start something new. Thousands may even now be standing on the brink of a pit they have dug with their own thoughts, words, and actions. For every one of them there may be a 'too late'. Don't get in a rut. Don't become old before you have tasted the full joy of magic.

Resolve now to do the things you have half-planned for weeks past, and refuse to be deterred by the **something that always turns up.**

'Time goes, you say, Ah, no!
Alas, Time stays, we go.'

I forget who said that, but you see what I mean. Time is a

precious thing, and you must make the most of it. Never be put off with the thought that you haven't the time. Magic is robbed of much of its power while you hold back from living. It comes easier and quicker when you are excited and happy about life.

What has passed when time has passed away? Opportunity has passed.

How are you going to make the most of the years that are given to you – that is your most vital problem today. Few people realize the value of their time until they come to the end of it. Then in desperation they think, 'Just fifteen minutes more, please.' They would give everything they possess to get one year more, one month more, five minutes more or another golden hour set with sixty diamond minutes. Every twenty-four minutes you can climb to the stars, or you can slide down into your own particular hell. This book is to help you climb to the stars, and the first essential is to put a value on **time**.

I am very **time conscious**. A magician has to be.

The studio clock is ticking round the last minute before I go on the air. My mind is a long way from the brilliantly lit scene of half a dozen stages all in one studio, this electronic miracle of television. I am thinking quietly of the millions of families who will be mentally linked with me in a few minutes. I am wondering how they will react to magic, which knows no barriers of time and distance.

Then I come out to the autograph seekers, the crowds who mob me for mementoes, who want only to grip me by the hand, or smile a 'thank you' for the wonderful performance.

It had been worth it. It wasn't a waste of time. Someone wants to do magic, someone wants to read minds, someone wants to see into the future. I have given them a glimpse of this magic. No, I never waste **Time**.

22
Help Through Your Hobby

I HAVE said much (you may think overmuch) on the supreme importance of utilizing your time to the utmost advantage in bringing out the magic of your mind. But I would not have you think for one moment that, in exhorting you to extract the full 'sixty seconds' worth of distance run' from every valuable minute, you should do so to the loss of a really worth-while hobby. Far from it. Your particular hobby may well be your consuming interest, and the recreational value of that interest can in itself assist you very considerably in developing your mental powers.

People's hobbies must of necessity differ very much according to the character of the person himself. What would appeal to one man might be the subject for ridicule in another. To make any hard-and-fast ruling as to what people should interest themselves in would not be feasible; one can only emphasize that the conscious mind should be allowed to relax at intervals so that the subconscious may take over; and so long as your hobby really does achieve that end for you personally, its precise nature is of no great account. Even so, the examination of other people's hobbies is not without interest, and there are some which **may** appeal to you yourself.

I like comedian Dave King's idea. He has set up an enormous model railway in his cellar, and made the surrounding countryside himself. He has thirteen or so locos and has built a little village of miniature houses. There are hills, valleys, and even churches. He is convinced that model trains are the most relaxing things in the world, and he spends much of his spare time with them. There are more than 700 feet of rails, and he is continuing them so that in the end they will extend through the walls into the underground rooms. You might laugh at the gasometer made out of an old tin, but it is very realistic.

Yes, Dave has a playtime, and it does him good. He is a great success both here and in America.

But why should you want to play with trains? And it's an understandable question. Well, I would say to that: 'Think of the concentration it entails; a concentration which may well be necessary to divorce the mind for a while from preying problems which the subconscious mind can tackle and resolve for one at the right time. When all his trains are working, Dave has to concentrate to avoid any accidents; keen concentration. And isn't this what you need to cultivate if you are going to be a clever magician? You can make your relaxation hours pay; they can help to bring out the magic in your mind.

This is no joke, truly. Your hobby can help you, if you choose wisely, as Dave King has done.

Model railway sales are running into 1,000,000 sets a year. Armies of grown-up men live in a Lilliputian world. Mr Macmillan has model trains, Lord Brabazon, Hughie Green, David Nixon, and Peter Cushing. Company director, Mr Walter Norris has a set reputed to be worth £75,000. You will not be alone in your interest.

Besides a keen interest in trains – toy trains and real trains – Peter Cushing would like to take a train-spotting holiday. Railways fascinate him.

Let's consider another hobby, which would also be helpful

to you as a magician. Peter has one of the most extensive collections of model soldiers. He has accumulated these 2¼-inch toy figures since he was a small boy. If you go into the studio of his home, you may find him inspecting the guard. He has about two thousand brightly coloured figures and one was specially made for him by a member of the British Society of Model Soldiers, to which he belongs. They range from before the Roman Empire to the 1914–18 war.

This wonderful collection is arranged in large glass-fronted cases the length of his studio. There are models forming a Coronation procession on one shelf, and the British Army through the ages on another.

In the largest case, Peter keeps his models **correct in every detail** and often useful references they are when a costume play comes along. These gay soldiers, which have to be seen to be believed, form a spectacular and arresting collection.

I like this hobby. It fosters **awareness** (all the different coloured uniforms) and the golden coach of the Coronation. A keen sense of **awareness** is what every magician must have; a keen observation that misses nothing. An eye for detail is so important, as I have impressed upon you before.

Certainly Peter is **aware**. When he was a little boy H. G. Wells would come and play with him. Wells was just as interested at playing soldiers as young Peter; he had, in fact, written a book for children to teach them how terrible war was. They had wonderful games together, which Peter says he will always remember.

The best form of recreation is one that incorporates your studies; like awareness, colour, concentration, and the observations of minute details.

You can enjoy your leisure and are learning at the same time; learning in this atmosphere of pageantry all about contemporary history. You are 'summing people up' and this time the 'people' are soldiers. You have something to show to your friends and something which is educating; something that brings relaxation to a tired mind.

The opposite of soldiers fighting is peace. Peace comes into your **purity** training and is absolutely essential to you as a magician. It is profound wisdom to think of things which are 'pure, lovely, and of good report'.

'But isn't there enough to do with the hundred and one things you tell us in this book?'

Time must be found for relaxation or you would break down nervously.

There are women eager to be magicians, and they should have their hobbies. I think there is nothing finer than that of Denise Robins, queen of romantic writers, with 130 novels to her name, including best-sellers **Heart of Paris** and **The Long Shadow**. Her hobby is the cultivation of roses. She even brought four rose bushes back from Brussels, as they make a speciality of a violet-hued rose. 'I can never wait for the first rose to appear,' she says. 'They are part of my life.'

What gave her this interest? 'I was initiated originally by my father-in-law who has won many prizes for roses at Chelsea,' says Denise.

You would be fascinated by the names of her roses: **Sultana, The Doctor, Virgo, Message, Sonata, Fantasia, Danse de Feu, Sterling Silver, Picture and Peace.** And such wonderful colours: **Scarlet, Orange, Apricot Pink, Golden Yellow, Deep Mauve, Sugar Pink.**

Date with a rose. Could there be anything lovelier? Denise tends them every day, in between bouts of writing. They are a great pleasure to her.

It was Dean Hole who said: '**He who would have beautiful Roses in his garden must have beautiful Roses in his heart.**'

I must remind you again that flowers are fifth-dimensional, and 5D is the plane on which a mental magician gets, or tries to get, in order to work magic of a spectacular kind. So a rose garden is a constant reminder of this, and the more often you tend them and admire their blossoms, the more often you are lifted up, and able to perform and make wonderful demonstrations. It is a grand hobby to have, a splendid form of relaxation. To grow a few roses, whatever hobby you may choose to have, is bound to be of benefit when it can lift you to another plane, if only momentarily. To see them is to love them, and loving them you (perhaps unconsciously) instruct the mind to reproduce pictures of them in the mind. The mind does so, and like this, impurity becomes crowded out. The more you love your roses and the more time you spend with them, the more pure you become.

Remember how I told you about the Rose of Life? I think Denise Robins must feel revived every time she sees her fabulous array of roses.

I switched on the radio a moment ago, and what did I hear? Nat Cole was singing **Rambling Rose**. A little while later somebody sang **The White Rose of Athens**, and **The Yellow Rose of Texas**, and this was followed by **Moonlight and Roses**. Even to hear people singing about roses makes you feel good.

Hobbies fill a gap. If you are frustrated in any way, there is some hobby to help you. No need to stew and make yourself sick with worry. Bring out the magic of your mind and focus your attention on something which will lift your spirit.

Charlie Wilson of Wembley had a great urge to write, but had no literary talent. What did he do? Believe it or not, he wrote up 37 plays and 154 sonnets and poems of William Shakespeare. It took him four years. He then wrote out the Bible, which took him five years to do. He writes these things as a hobby while his three sisters watch television.

Charles is a clerk in a sporting news agency, but that didn't satisfy him. **He wanted to be a writer.** Realizing he had no talent for it, he overcame his frustration in this most strange way. He gained fame for his writing, and this made him happy.

And here is another story. Tom Barber of Hastings had both his legs amputated. But he has not let it get him down. He is full of enthusiasm for his hobby, which is collecting key fobs. He has four hundred of them from all over the world. Unique in his collection is a musical one from Switzerland, and one in real gold from the Nevada Desert in the form of gold-mining implements. He understands the psychology of overcoming a terrible disability, and has brought the magic out of his mind, keeping himself young in mind and bright in spirit, an inspiration to all who meet him. Could you do that if you lost both legs? Magic works wonders, as you would know if you saw this happy man.

Morecambe and Wise, the well-known stage and television comedians, are keen tegestologists (beer mat collectors). They have a huge collection which they keep in their homes. Half of it is in Eric Morecambe's London home, the other half in Ernie Wise's lovely home in Peterborough. They are honorary presidents of the British Beer Mat Collector's Society. An interesting hobby, but has it any psychological value? Indeed, yes. With each new mat the sun of **awareness** increasingly breaks through. You are aware of the great number of varieties in beer mats, and this leads you to notice and become conscious of variation in other things, too, because you have trained your eyes to be keen. I have impressed upon you the importance of observation and in noticing details, and a hobby which can help you in this is going to help you with your magic.

It isn't everybody who has a hobby, but amongst those who do are all types of people.

One of the most interesting, I think, is Harry Edwards, the well-known spiritual healer, whose beautiful sanctuary is at Burrows Lea. Harry is just over seventy but looks many years younger. Every week, year after year, the lame, the sick, and the blind come to him to be relieved of pain, stiffness, and locked joints, and wonderful cures take place. He receives anything up to two thousand letters a week, answers them in forty-eight hours, and there are fine demonstrations to report.

Harry writes articles for the **Spiritual Healer** and is the author of five remarkable books, including **Psychic Healing,** a 'must' for anyone interested in healing.

Someone says of him: 'I can't think of anyone he would disapprove of. There is a capacity to love every living thing in this man that would simply disintegrate him if it did not find expression in his wonderful work. His home is filled with beauty, flowers, and his pictures (which, he says, he sometimes stays up at night to paint).'

You might call Harry Edwards a dedicated man, and like all dedicated people, he is very happy.

And what is his hobby? How does he find relaxation? I am pleased to tell you – **it is magic.** He is quite clever at it, as he started practising magic before he became a spiritual healer, which is some good time ago now. Amongst other things he does the **watch in loaf** magic, and there are times when he performs at public functions. He thinks that acuteness and awareness are two of the most helpful things in performing magic. It's rather wonderful, don't you think, that such an intensely busy man, and one who does such noble work, can make time for magic? It delights me. I would like to hear of more people making time for magic, because when you take an interest in real magic, you begin to interest yourself in **mental** magic. The world would be a much better place if it were peopled with magicians of that nature.

Women choose unusual hobbies. Diana Pulson, writing in the **Liverpool Daily Post,** tells of a woman, the wife of a chemist, who collects walking sticks. You see, in the olden days, they were hung around the walls to ward off evil spirits. In the morning they would wipe the sticks to take off the evil spirits that were gathered around it, as they thought.

Mrs Grace Hughes has forty-nine or more, and has been offered big money for them. They are mostly **glass** walking sticks, probably dandy sticks used by the men-about-town of the eighteenth century. Because they are made with a twirl of glass, twisted like giant barley-sugar sticks, they glitter and gleam in the sunlight, or when the electric light is turned on. She has collected these over a period of fifteen years and they give her great pleasure.

Have you had a hobby for fifteen years? It eases your mind to be absorbed in something; to see something you collect building up, and to see the excitement on a visitor's face. Everyone should have an interest that they can indulge in as relaxation. Many hobbies are put on exhibition, sometimes good money offered, and certainly fame.

Why do I want you to have a hobby, when really this is a book on how to bring the magic out of your mind? Because I don't want you to be weighed down with nagging worries; a hobby takes your mind off things and gives the subconscious a chance to 'take over'. It is constructive. It gives the mind something positive to hold on to. You can't be miserable, harassed, and hopelessly fed up whilst you have an interesting hobby to turn to.

What are **my** interests? **Tropical fish** and **poodles.**

23
Observing The Wonderful

COLLIE KNOX, the well-known author and columnist, tells the story of a night at the theatre, when a man came in and seated himself next to him. He reminds us that he did not turn to look at him, actually the curtain was rising, but that he sensed at once that, when he did see him face to face, he would see a man he would very much like to know.

Then he goes on to say how all eyes in the great audience turned upwards to the Royal Box. Her Royal Highness the Queen came in, glittering with diamonds and precious jewels. She was magnificently dressed.

The story continues. Everybody sat down, except the man beside him, who stood for a while longer, gazing enraptured at what he saw.

'Wonderful. **Wonderful,**' he said softly to himself. 'Worth coming over for; she looks marvellously young.'

Then we are told that he had just come to this country from America. There was nothing like this in the U.S.A.

This is where I take over. You will note that he was observant to a degree; he had to remain standing a little while longer. He **saw** things; he didn't just notice them. He had the capacity to recapture for one glorious moment the radiant happiness of a child, and which most of us have lost. The art of marvelling was expressed in those two words: Wonderful. **Wonderful.**

When you are a child your senses are vibrantly alive to every passing stimulus. The magic of a windswept sea of bluebells, a patch of daisies on the lawn (I wonder who first decided that daisies shouldn't grow on lawns?), a spider's web bejewelled with sparkling morning dew, a new moon, the sunset.

For a child, the world is a wonderful place, endlessly exciting, full of magic. You grow older and tend to forget that the world is a wonderful place, still full of magic if you have eyes to see it.

You have to become as a little child again. Never has life been so full of magic as it is today with the marvels of radio, television, telstar, marvellous cures, and many other things. It is important that you should be conscious of all the magic around you. This will create the enthusiasm to go further and seek fresh magic.

Magic must be made every day, that is the point to remember. Then you, too, can say with feeling, **'Wonderful.'**

The first step is to **see** things, not just notice them. Observe. Really observe.

How long is it since you saw the sun rise, watched with wonder while the sky turns a magnificent hue and the tree-tops gleam suddenly with gold?

Have you been out at the very beginning of a spring day and seen the wonder of it? Daybreak, more magic than moonlight, more beautiful than any other hour at any other time, is wonderful.

How much have you been missing? There is the dawn chorus, dew on the grass, and some people – the ever young – **dance,** yes **dance,** barefoot in the dew. This is good, you get vibrations from the earth. Have you tasted these pleasures?

Magic starts early, whilst most of us are asleep in bed. But some there are who would not dream of missing the glory of it.

You have been given in this century of modern miracles an opportunity to restore your sense of wonder, and from that sense of wonder you can bring out the magic in your mind. You must cultivate the art of observation, an art which Conan Doyle made so prominent in his Sherlock Holmes stories. His hero-detective saw the most insignificant things – the tell-tale stub of a cigarette, a piece of hair on the lapel of a coat, a spot of mud on a slipper, little things which to others go unseen.

Train your eyes to see, not just notice things. Keen observation brings wonderment.

How can you train your eyes to see? Follow the Yogis. To bring out the magic in your mind and to be able to see wonderful things, you must cultivate awareness. The Yogis, famous for doing such magical feats, practise awareness in a very simple way. They train themselves to become conscious of what they see, by thinking of what they are doing and looking at. They repeat to themselves such things as:

I am walking by a river.
I am reading a book.
I am riding on a bus.
I am sweeping the floor.
I am walking upstairs.
I am looking through the window.
I am writing a letter.
I am combing my hair – and so on.

And they will repeat again and again such things as:

A bird is singing.
Baby is sleeping.
The band is playing.
That is a car.
This is a magnifying glass.
The clock is ticking – and so on.

You may think, 'What a tragedy to go through life saying: "Oh yes, that's the sun, that's the moon, there are the stars, that is a tree," and then when it is time for you to leave this earth, to realize that it has been all words, and you haven't really seen anything at all.'

This is not so. The repetition of a word that represents what you are looking at, hammers it home to your subconscious, and the time comes when you do not have to speak the word, because you are observant to a degree. It is very simple, but it is a necessity if you want to develop your powers of observation.

> What is this life if, full of care,
> We have no time to stand and stare?

So wrote the poet W. H. Davis. He was well known as a tramp who observed things. The wildest magic never conjured up for Aladdin more wonder than that spread before you in this era. **Stand and stare.**

Observe as a little child, and use your imagination. I was walking one day with a little boy in the country and we came to some hedges white with hawthorn. He looked at them and smiled, 'Little ballerinas,' he said.

Only a child can see dragon scales on tree trunks, fairy faces in dew drops, and heaven on earth in a plastic bucket of mud.

How can you speak of wonderful things like **little ballerinas**, if you cannot see magic in anything?

The first need of our age is to restore to men and women their wonder at the universe and at their place in it; to restore their belief in magic, and that they can dare nobly and conquer. This is the task of every psychologist.

Read your Bible and study the Greatest Psychologist of all. He observed. He **saw** life in the dead Lazarus, sight in the blind, and health in the sick. The Book is full of magic and wonder.

If you have never read your Bible, start to read it now for the first time.

The first time! The first time is always so wonderful. The first bird notes in the dawn, your first bath in warm scented water, your first ride on a bicycle.

Think of the pleasure of eating strawberries before they are cheap enough for everybody to eat them. Think what a thrill it is eating the first dish of peas while they are still dear. Think of seeing the golden sands or the sun-kissed ocean for the first time. Your first 'I love you.' Your first little dinner after the show.

The first time brings out the magic in your mind, and you are able to speak of wonderful things.

I remember someone writing in the Press about Princess Alexandra's wedding. It read:

'What a beautiful bride! What a wonderful wedding! After the long, hard winter, the dreary news, the strikes, the pictures of unpleasant politicians and unwashed marchers, let us thank God for this handsome couple whose wedding brought colour and beauty into our lives.'

When you speak of wonderful things like that you feel good, young, and friendly. You look forward to things. But so many people are, by the end of the day, fed up, worn out, bad-tempered, and irritable. They have 'had it'. They are too tired to observe.

This feeling of tiredness comes from monotony, the eternal sameness of life as they are living it. They should try to take their minds off the commonplace now and again, and observe. They would never become bored once they began to use their eyes.

You want to work magic in your life? Remember the great psychological truth that **like attracts like.** Determine to look for magic all around you, contemplate for a considerable time, not notice it only, and the attraction which comes from this recognition will reinforce the magic in your mind, and your appreciation of it will bring it out into the open. And when you see something magical, like the marvel of television, don't grumble so much at a bad picture. There are still hundreds of people not so lucky as you; people who don't possess one. Ask such a person to come and view along with you, and watch their excitement and thrill along with them. Speak

253

of it as **wonderful**. If you don't like that one particular pro-gramme, you can still appreciate the magic of how it comes to appear on your screen. Your grandparents and great-great-grandparents knew nothing of these wonders.

I know a man who wanted television but he lived in a caravan, and the site where he lived was not wired for electricity, so he couldn't have one.

He bought himself a telescope, the biggest he could afford. He put it through the skylight of his van. Like this he studied the stars, and this brought him to reading all he could about astronomy. His excitement was terrific. What limitless wonder is in the heavens. The sky was full of magic.

When people see him they say, 'He looks as though he enjoys life.' Maybe they say it with a certain tone of envy. Ask him about the stars and he will explain from his heart, 'Wonderful. **Wonderful.**'

He looks for magic through a telescope, and a whole new world opens up to him.

Another man looks through a microscope at a strand of hair, a piece of cotton, a spot of blood, ash from his cigarette, or anything else he fancies. It is magnified to reveal what he could never see with his naked eye, and what he sees is **magic**. A great transformation takes place. His eyes sparkle, his countenance lights up, and his whole being is radiant. Not only is he alive, but manifestly glad to be alive. A whole new world has opened up for him, too. Because he can **see**.

When I let my dog out in the morning he stands for a moment at the open door, sniffs in the air, drinks in the sight, sounds, and smells for a while. It is as though so much magic hits him all at once and he is bowled over by it.

Then suddenly he capers around, leaps in the air, and I know that he is aware of the electric excitement of the great outdoors and all that's in it. Why can't we be the same?

A piece of paper blowing along the pavement, a raindrop splashing on baby's pram, these are magic to a child. He **sees** them, which is quite different from just noticing them.

You can bring out the magic in your mind if you keep your sense of wonder. You may be in love, when life is full of magic, but all too soon you lower your eyes from the glittering stars to the level of burnt toast on the breakfast table, account books and washing-machines. And the sky is no longer a soft blue. You don't even notice it!

These moments that make you catch your breath and say, 'Wonderful! **Wonderful!**' are the moments that come from a keen observation. It is the moment when you really see something, and don't simply notice it as you pass by.

It is called ecstasy and is as elusive as a butterfly. But to a person who knows how to bring the magic out of his mind, such moments fill the day.

A pilot I know was trying to tell me how he feels when he flies high above the clouds. He couldn't put it into words. A diver, plunging deep into crystal-clear water feels the same. He couldn't put it into words. It is ecstasy. It is what the American felt when he gazed at the Queen in all her splendour.

Children know this ecstasy when it rains. They do not run away from it. They paddle in every puddle they can find, and life is wonderful. A grown-up will say, 'Why doesn't Fred have the sense to come in out of the rain?' But in the world of magic, it is the shelterers who are the senseless ones.

Robert Blatchford tells the story of how, one day in camp, he watched the sunset, when a young doctor asked him what he was staring at. When he said the sunset, the doctor asked why.

'Isn't it worth looking at?' asked Blatchford.

The doctor smiled, raised his eyebrows, and answered: 'Well, now I notice it; it **is** pretty.'

The sunset – now he noticed it – was pretty! And he goes on to remind us that that young, educated man had never **seen** the sunset; he had only noticed it; and he could not describe it, he could only call it pretty.

It is the same with most people. They are unobservant. It is as though their eyes had fallen inside. They do not **see** a

255

thing. They only notice it. And for them there is no magic. Open your awareness to the wonder-world of the things which in your everyday life you have never had time to see. Don't be aware of people. You can be daily reduced to wretchedness by the too-close proximity of your fellow men. Forget people; leave them out of your consciousness for a while, and observe alone – quietly alone.

A little boy brought his mother a sea-shell from off the sands, and he was marvelling at it. It seemed a very ordinary shell, but the little boy saw it very differently. He was excited by its shape, its delicate colouring, the magic he thought he heard as he held it to his ear.

His mother looked at his father as they lounged in their deck chairs and said, 'What happens to us when we grow up, Robert?'

She realized in that moment that they didn't thrill over little things any more; didn't observe beauty.

Krishnamurti writes in his **Commentaries on Living**:

'The other day, walking along Westminster Embankment, I picked up a little stone or pebble, that had perhaps fallen from some lorry carrying a load of gravel. It was so smooth and beautiful with its strange markings, that I slipped it into my pocket. I have carried it about ever since, bringing it out at odd moments to look at it and meditate upon its mystery. . . .'

He observed a little stone. Do you ever stop to look at a fragment like this when you take a walk? When you observe to this extent, you are able to speak of wonderful things, like the little boy with the sea-shell, when he came running up to his mother.

It is always the magician who perceives the wonderful. He asks you to observe closely, and from seemingly nowhere you will see a white dove appear, sometimes a dozen white doves; in fact a fountain full of doves, in one case. Or it may be a rabbit, a bunch of flowers, a mass of coloured silk hand-kerchiefs. If you are determined to be a magician, start right now to perceive the wonders around you. Get into the habit of it; observe and observe until you have endless wonders to talk about. Make your audience excited, enchanted, even if it's only in your home circle.

Do you remember some long while ago television's **At Home** visit to the Belgrave house of Mrs Gerald Legge, as she was then. I am speaking of the Countess of Dartmouth, that very beautiful woman who has a very psychological outlook.

You will remember that everything was **'absolute heaven'**, **'madly gay'**, **'terribly sweet'**.

Berkeley Smith admired everything – the furniture, pieces of china, silver, and his hostess's dress. She replied, 'Oh, d'you like it? **How very sweet of you.'**

Her vitality was irresistible. She said, 'I suppose I'm terribly interested in everything. I **feel**, terribly strongly, that when one is lucky they should help others who are not so well off.'

A friend of mine saw her once on television, and she said she had on the most beautiful dress she had ever seen, and everything she said was gay and wonderful.

Here is a lady who sees the best in everything.

Nicholas Monserrat, the famous novelist, is another who possesses this quality. You remember, he wrote **The Cruel Sea**.

He was determined that Phillipa Crosby, known as **The Cruel She**, and who wrote a waspish gossip column, should be the same. Phillipa beat up society in her column. Everyone bought the paper for her page. (Oh, how **awful** to say a thing like that about **Mary**.)

When Phillipa fell in love, she changed. She gave up her old ways. She burned her slings and arrows and brought out bouquets instead.

Under Monserrat's influence she began to see the best in everybody, and she built them up instead of slapping them down. She now began to settle happily into the business of finding something nice to say about almost everything. Everybody spoke of her now as a charming person. The hotel where she was staying was **marvellous**, and the service so **friendly and reliable**. A film star of whom she used to say rather mean things in her column was now described as **a perfect lamb**.

She never used a harsh word any more; Phillipa, the terror of the town, was behind her for ever. She sharpened her perception and saw the best in everything and everybody. This transformation was **magic**.

Fred Astaire, that fabulous film star, whose autobiography and records are said to sell in thousands a day, is another who has a keen sense of observation. Everyone marvels at his youth, with fifty-two dancing years behind him, he still looks, feels, and acts young. What does he say? 'I approach everything as if it were **fresh**.' '**As if it were fresh. . . .**' That's the obvious Astaire secret.

'The man is absolutely ageless,' says M.G.M. producer Arthur Freed. 'Why, I'm only a couple of years older than he is and I look like his grandfather.'

You can't look at everything as though it were **fresh**, unless you really observe; look deep into a thing. For Fred Astaire, this ability to observe has given him eternal youth. He never seems to grow a day older, and he can still dance, while others are ready to drop.

A reporter tells of how he spoke over the phone from London to Jayne Mansfield, the famous cinema star, filming in Dubrovnik.

'Hullo Jayne, how are you?

'And how's Mickey?'

'He's **wonderful, fabulous. . . .**'

'**Wonderful, fabulous. . . .**' the reporter repeated.

'I'm so happy, I'm fortunate in having such a **wonderful** husband and three **beautiful** children.'

Then she continued: 'When this picture is finished I might make another one called **Cleopatra Slept Here**.'

'**Wonderful, fabulous,**' the reporter called back. You see, he had 'caught on' to her excitement, just as Phillipa 'caught'

Nicholas Monserrat's enthusiasm. Everything was so **wonderful**. And when you **think** like that, you **feel** like that. And when you **feel** like that, you're living, really living. The rest of the world are dead ducks!

Do you switch on your television morning, noon and night, and never hear the radio any more? Or are you one of the lucky ones who a little while ago heard Bob and Alf Pearson ('My Brother and I'), the famous duettists, singing the 1963 winning tune in the Eurovision Song Contest?

> **Say wonderful things to me,**
> **I think you're wonderful, too. . . .**

This was sung with great feeling, as only Bob and Alf know how. It was deeply beautiful, and sums up all that I am trying to tell you.

> **Say wonderful things to me,**
> **I think you're wonderful, too. . . .**

What a different world it would be, wouldn't it? Try it. You'll be a magician **par excellence**.

What did they say of the Great Psychologist and Magician? **'And his name shall be called wonderful'** (Is. 9. 6).

24
Prelude To Mind-Reading— Physiognomy

WOULD you like to read the mind of your bank manager? You would. But you don't believe it possible. You don't believe there is such a thing as mind-reading. You don't believe you can look at a person, and in the flash of an eyelid, know what he's thinking.

Two people start humming a tune at the same time, and you say this is coincidence. The question your husband answers before you have asked him, is that coincidence, too? Of course it isn't. It is one mind contacting the other.

You believe in electricity, X-rays, the radio, and television. There was a time when people laughed at the very idea of such possibilities, as you are laughing now.

You believe in artificial organs in the body because you have read wonderful cases about them in the newspapers. You believe in the telephone, because you picked up the receiver only last night and had a word with Bill. You believe in colour photography, because the snaps you took on your summer holiday came out in lovely colours, and you saw it with your own eyes. You believe in nuclear energy (nobody will let you forget it), the airliner that carries over a hundred people, centrifugal force, telstar in orbit, and the jelly fish. But you don't believe in mind-reading. Really, you astonish me.

Your mind can span great distances, and know what the other man is thinking. Many people have had instances of this. They have done something or written something, to coincide with what someone at a distance has wished. They have caught that thought in the other person's mind, and acted on it at precisely the exact moment. This has often been proved to be true.

Some people have a natural gift for contacting other minds, but they fall short now and again, because they haven't troubled to develop it. They don't really think about it, or marvel at it. If they happen to catch another's thought, they smile and leave it at that, instead of trying to cultivate an inborn power which could be of enormous help to them.

Right from a young boy I was able to tell what my mother and father were thinking. I might have made a mistake now and again, as everyone does with any art when it's untrained, but my parents recognized at once that I was not quite like other boys. They did everything humanly possible to encourage and help my development along these lines. From an early age I commenced to read and study all books on what I call 'mind stuff'. One forgets things with the passing of time, **but the subconscious never forgets,** and all this knowledge has been stored up over the years to come to my aid in a thousand different ways.

As a prelude to mind-reading, I advise every man and woman to read over and over again the sort of books that give you a deep insight into other people's lives and the working of the mind; autobiographies, psychology, physiognomy, and so on.

Study character, because what you observe of a person's character is often an indication to the sort of thoughts he will be thinking. Study character to such an extent that in one quick look, you can 'sum up' a person. You will know, for instance, whether he or she is a selfish or unselfish type, an earthy or idealistic personality. Shall we study character together, and see how it works out; how it is likely to help

261

you get a grasp of the sort of thought that runs through a certain person's mind.

You cannot become skilful in character reading unless you develop a systematic technique, and this is where your power of observation comes in. As soon as you really and truly start **observing** people, you can use your technique profitably. You have to have a keen interest in the person whose mind you want to read, even if it's only momentary interest. Your concentration must be focussed upon that one person so that you shut out all else. This over-all observance registers with you so that you know what sort of thought to expect. This is only when you have studied character to such an extent that an instantaneous glance is enough.

Centuries ago, Aristotle studied physiognomy and found it intensely interesting. He was intrigued. It is just as fascinating today.

When I am face to face with someone, it is the eyes which tell me all I need to know about the owner's past, present, or future. It is the eyes which give me a good indication of what is in the mind. You should make a study of them and you will find them a great help to mind-reading. People talk with their eyes. In one quick glance a girl can convey 'You and I ought to get together.' It's easy to read what's in her mind; she has told you half of it already!

Eye talking is an intimate technique and used in a crowded room can be very effective. 'See you tonight, sometime?' can be asked without a word being spoken, and in silence her eyes can convey the answer.

Eyes are a wonderful thing to study; their shape, their size, their colour – each has a separate meaning and invaluable to any student of mind-reading. What one kind of person thinks is very different to that of another. The optimistic type thinks differently to the pessimist; the healthy differently to the sick; the rich differently to the poor; the criminal differently to the virtuous. It is not easy to figure it all out with any speed, but practice makes perfect. I have had years of studying people since I started on all this as a small boy, and if you would bring out the magic in your mind, start now. Notice the people in the bus, in the train, in the bar, across the restaurant table. Practise. Practise. Practise. Make your observations a daily ritual and never stop practising, until it is a real part of you. Notice a person front-face, side-face, and from the back. Don't miss any little detail that can make the interpretation faithful. You should spend quite half an hour a day doing it regularly every week. In time it will be safe to make a lightning judgment, but it takes a long time before you can be dead sure. The day will come when you can 'tell at a glance'.

The eyes are the most important of all, because it is impossible for the eyes not to betray your thinking. If your bank manager has small eyes, he will be obstinate and shrewd. If he has roving eyes (continually looking here and there away from you) then he will not have the slightest interest in you, only so much as you can serve him. If you look at him to mind-read, you may be sure his thoughts are, 'What do you think of me?' He is only interested in himself, so you have that much to work on.

Your bank manager may have 'an open countenance', a 'stern look', 'shifty eyes'. Or he may have eyes that say 'beetle off'. I wouldn't know. But if it's the latter, you hurry home to your wife and say, 'He didn't half give me a look!'

You may have eyes that beg for mercy, but we are not concerned with you. We are concerned with the bank manager and what he is thinking.

Wide eyes indicate a readiness for quick response, and it is to be hoped that your bank manager has this particular feature. It helps with the overdraft.

Has he a 'weak chin', a 'strong jaw', or what physiognomists call 'sexual lips'? If it's the latter, better take your pretty wife along so that he will forget the overdraft altogether!

Most people can be regarded as belonging to one of the four basic groups, when it comes to faces. The **Melancholic,** the **Aggressive,** the **Lethargic,** the **Frank.** There are many other types, but these are the main ones. I won't describe the shape of their faces, but each type is represented by a certain shape of face and you must study each individual type, until you know it off by heart. The hair and the colour of the hair matter. If she's a lovely blonde, maybe you're right when you mind-read and say she's thinking **Diamonds are a girl's best friend!**

The hands are a very special part of the body to reflect personality. A hand in movement expresses the inner thought. How many hands do you shake in the course of your life? And you haven't even noticed them! You must observe; observe in detail. The nice, the big, the ugly; all convey valuable truths that can assist you in mind-reading. Observe the hands of those around you. Interpretation will help you a lot. Notice thumbs, those that stick out and are bent over, the thumb of a very self-willed person, and those hidden in a clenched fist, belonging to the type that has little or no will-power. A dead person, when all will-power has gone, often has a thumb hidden like this. If your bank manager sits at his desk with his thumb hidden in the palm of his hand like this, you may open a second and third account, for he has no will to stop you! But bank managers are not like that, as you will observe. Each little clue is of vital importance in your observation.

All great portrait painters know the importance of the hand; so does the doctor and the surgeon. It can tell a thousand stories and do much to help you understand a character and know what clues to work on when trying to read his mind.

John Ralph, writing in the **Sunday Graphic:**

'. . . **Because although Koran himself will not claim that his brilliant act is based on telepathy, I still think he would be a gift to the scientists.**

Why? Because I think he may have powers which he does not himself realize. . . .

. . . I asked him if he had ever offered himself as a subject to the scientists investigating mind-reading in this country. He had not.

Would he? He would not.'

And under the illustration of my picture:

'What secret lies behind the eyes of Al Koran?'

The eyes. The eyes. Learn to read the eyes first. It is an index to the mind.

25
Prelude To Mind-Reading— Numerology

Do you believe that a certain number is lucky for you, or that a certain number, as far as you are concerned, has a hoodoo on it? If you believe this, then you will find the study of numerology a fascinating one. And I want you to study the science of numbers. It gives you a strong indication of a person's personality; his likes and dislikes, his characteristics. And a profound knowledge of these things, if you can spot them instantly, is an enormous help to you in mind-reading.

Do numbers affect what a person thinks? To a certain extent it does; it gives you a clue to the kind of thought that that particular person holds.

I once picked a woman out of the audience and said, 'You look like a three.' She said she wasn't. 'Yes, you're a three,' I added. And this was found to be true. She did not understand numerology. I did. And I was right. And because she was a three; I had insight into many things about her.

I will invite a lady out of the audience to come on to the stage. I will hand her a box and ask her to write the name of someone close to her and put it in the box, and we lock it up. Then I will tell her, 'You have three boys and a girl. The girl's name is Caroline. We'll open the box.' And there, sure enough, is the name for all to see. How did I know the number of her family? I leave you guessing. But I was right.

Numerology is a recognized science. One may not profess to understand it, or even think that it works, but most of us have got to admit that certain numbers do appear to have magic in our lives, whilst others seem to bring misfortune.

How do you know your lucky and unlucky numbers? A study of numerology will tell you that. And it's easily understood. There are many fine books on the subject.

What I want to do is to fire your enthusiasm. I want to get you really interested, because if part of your magic is going to be mind-reading, you must follow me. I have made a deep study of it.

Have you a lucky number that you are conscious of? Perhaps it's seven or five, or maybe you plump for some out-of-the-way number like 172?

Ting Shaochen, a Chinese footballer, disliked fours, because they had the same pronunciation as the word 'death'.

When he drew a national lottery ticket with the number 324,504, he changed it for a ticket without a four.

The draw took place and ticket number 324,504 won first prize worth £20,000.

Four was his number, whether he liked it or not, and he should never have changed it. Talk about money to a man like that, and you know what is in his mind all right. Or you can get pretty near it.

Yana, one of the most beautiful singers on stage and television today, says that all numbers in her life must be divisible by four. She likes to eat things by fours; eat four sandwiches, take four swallows at a drink, put four flowers in a vase, and so on. She believes four is lucky for her. Take a number four person out for a drink, even if she doesn't take four sips, you may be sure she will ask for four drinks. Know the characteristics of a number four person, and you have a clue to the kind of thoughts they think.

Four may be your unlucky number complex. Someone

dear to you died on the fourth, you became ill on the thirteenth (one plus three makes four) and as a result of your illness you lose your job – yes, on the fourth of the month. You feel dogged by that unlucky number. You become gripped to such an extent that you actually feel nervous every time a date with a four in it comes round. Silly, isn't it?

Let us consider the four in forty. Forty appears frequently in Scripture. Moses was forty days in the mount; Elijah was forty days fed by ravens; the rain of the flood for forty days; Noah opened the window of the ark in another forty days.

Doesn't it make you think? Doesn't it make you want to study numbers?

Let's carry on. Forty days was the period of embalming; Ninevah had forty days to repent; our Lord rested forty days; it was forty days after His resurrection when he was seen.

Forty was not chosen haphazard; there is a good reason for it.

St Swithin's betokens forty days' rain or dry weather. A quarantine extends to forty days.

The ancient physicians ascribe many strange changes to the period of forty; the alchemists looked on forty days as the charmed period when the philosopher's stone and elixir of life were to appear.

You are bound to agree that numbers have an immense significance. If I bore you, you can take 'forty winks'.

Lucky Jack Hylton of the golden touch was the first man to buy a Premium Bond. His bond was number eleven; numbers one to ten were presented to ten leading citizens.

'Eleven is my lucky number,' he said. 'I am sixty-five next year – add six and five and you get eleven.'

Then he went out and put £10 on **Loppylugs** in the Cambridgeshire Stakes at Newmarket. It won at 100–7.

See what I mean?

Do you know the numbers of your friends and relations; the numbers of your office staff, your workmates, your tradesmen, the vicar, your doctor? Of course you don't, you have never bothered. Why should you? But as a magician, particularly one who is going to do the biggest magic of all – mind-reading – you must never cease to try and find out everything humanly possible about those around you. It will aid you in reading the minds of other people.

Numbers are used in business. The magazine *FATE* was so-called because, according to numerology, the letters F.A.T.E. add up to fourteen. One plus four is five – the numeral identified with travel. The subject matter of Fate includes space travel. The magazine travels widely in this country and abroad.

The number fourteen is also inclusive of seven (two times seven equals fourteen) and seven is a very lucky number, historically, religiously, and mundanely, as all dice-shooters know!

It is a common practice among sailors to add up the ship's number. Lloyd's Registry shows all seagoing vessels to have a number. A ship number that adds to seven is an indication of a 'lucky' ship. A ship number which adds up to five means a long voyage and much travel. If the total number comes to eight or six it means uproar and unsafe, and when sailors discover this, they put in a transfer.

You didn't know that numbers make all the difference; that they have great significance? Well, I'm telling you these stories to impress you with a desire to study numerology, because I know how helpful it is going to be to you.

Ann Todd, the beautiful stage and film star, believes that all the big things in her life go in sevens. She went to Hollywood on the 27th of the month, opened at the Saville theatre on the 17th, had seven operations, and played the lead in **The Seventh Veil** film. She wears a lucky seven on her bangle.

If you visit Ann Todd in her dressing-room there will be a large gilt and red seven on the door. Do you realize that there are seven letters in her name?

Number seven became part of the life of J. L. Whorton of Memphis. His father was one of seven children and so was his mother. He was a seventh son, he had seven brothers and seven sisters, and seven brothers-in-law and seven sisters-in-law.

His wife had seven brothers and sisters, and he had seven sons and seven grandchildren.

Don't dabble on the surface of this science, make an extensive study of it.

Seven is a mystic or sacred number; it is composed of four and three, which, among the Pythagoreans, were, and from time immemorial have been, accounted lucky numbers.

There are seven days in creation, seven days in the week, seven graces, seven divisions in the Lord's Prayer, seven ages in the life of man, climacteric years are seven and nine with their multiples by odd numbers, and in religion it continues.

Naaman was commanded to dip seven times in Jordan; Elijah sent his servant seven times to look for rain; ten times seven Israelites go to Egypt; the exile lasts the same number of years, and there were ten times seven elders. Pharaoh in his dream saw seven kine and seven ears of corn, seven priests with seven trumpets marched round Jericho once every day, but seven times on the seventh day; Samson's wedding feast lasted seven days.

In the Apocalypse we have seven churches of Asia, seven candlesticks, seven stars, seven trumpets, seven spirits, seven horns, seven vials, seven plagues, a seven-headed monster, and a lamb with seven eyes.

The old astrologers and alchemists recognized seven planets, and from this very ancient belief sprang the theory that man was composed of seven substances, and has seven natures.

There are Seven Champions; the patron saints of England, Scotland, Wales, Ireland, France, Spain, and Italy. The Seven Sorrows of Mary, Seven times Christ spoke on the Cross, Seven Wonders of the World, and so on.

Frank Crew, the well-known author and columnist, says, 'There has always figured in the important and favourable events in my life the figure three. I have lived in the third cottage along a lane, and lived in a luxury flat numbered three, and I had to take a thirty bus home. I was married on the third at twelve o'clock (one and two is three).

'When anything good and important comes on the post it arrives on the third or the thirteenth or thirtieth of the month, on the three o'clock post. Yes, it's true. When editors and publishers commission my work, they have always done so on a letter dated the third, or a multiple of three.

'Three is the number of the Trinity, and is said to be a very good number. I have proved this to be perfectly true in my own life. The best review I ever received for one of my books had words which when totalled and the digits added together, came to three. My dog's birthday was on the third, and she died on the third.

'So often have I counted the numbers on bus tickets only to find that the digits added together totalled three, that I have long since ceased to count them. If somebody sends me a snapshot, two more letters follow with snapshots. If somebody sends me a book, I know that two more books are on the way, for everything in my life goes in threes. The big things and the little things.'

Interesting, isn't it?

Pythagoras calls three the perfect number, expressive of 'beginning, middle, and end', wherefore he makes it a symbol of Deity. The Brahmins represent their god with three heads; the world was supposed by the ancients to be under the rule of three gods, Jupiter, Neptune, and Pluto. The Fates are three, the Furies three, the Graces three; the fountain from which Nylas drew water was presided over by three nymphs. Man is threefold, body, soul, and spirit; the world is threefold, earth, sea, and air; the enemies of man are threefold, the world, the flesh, and the devil; the Christian graces are threefold, Faith, Hope, and Charity; the kingdoms of Nature are threefold, mineral, vegetable, and animal; the cardinal colours are three in number, red, yellow and blue. The three tongues, those in which the inscription on the Cross were written, Hebrew, Greek, and Latin. Job had three friends (Job 2. 11); Abraham was accosted by three men (angels) (Gen. 18. 2); Nebuchadnezzar cast three men into the fiery furnace (Dan. 3. 24); Moses was hidden three months (Exod. 2. 2); Samson mocked Delilah three times (Judg. 16. 15); Elijah stretched himself three times on the child which he restored to life (1 Kings 17. 21). The great famine in David's reign lasted three years (2 Sam. 21. 1); so did the great drought in Ahab's reign (Luke 6. 25). There were three men transfigured on the mount, and three spectators (Matt. 17. 1–4). Every ninth wave is said to be the largest (three times three is nine). And there are very many more which I have not listed.

Jerry Desmonde, the famous stage and film star, came to believe that thirteen was very lucky for him. He felt so sure of this that he insisted on the final 'e' in Desmonde, to give his stage name the lucky thirteen letters.

Peter Cushing, the famous star of stage, screen and television, is convinced of it too.

He likes to occupy room thirteen, and picks number thirteen for his theatre seat, and his reservations in aeroplanes.

'Something wonderful always happens to me on a Friday 13th,' he says. 'Year after year there is always some nice surprise on that date.'

Douglas Venner's lucky number was thirty-one. At the age of thirty-one he took thirty-one people thirty-one miles in a thirty-one-seater coach to support an application to run thirty-one tours with his motor coaches in thirty-one days. **The application was granted.**

He was luckier than a fireworks firm in Chile, who decided to reorganize their concern without the number thirteen.

After an explosion which killed eight, the owner explained that the street number was thirteen, the explosion occurred on November 13th, and the employees had been increased to thirteen on that day. They decided afterwards to reorganize their concern without the number thirteen.

Strange, but perfectly true.

Thirteen is not your number, you wouldn't choose it; nothing would make you buy a house with thirteen on the door.

You get the idea because nearly two thousand years ago thirteen sat down to the Last Supper on the first Maundy Thursday.

The Italians never use the number in their lotteries, and in Paris no house bears it.

An ecstatically happy young couple, newly wed, arrived in a taxi at their honeymoon hotel in New York. Nothing seemed to mar their joy.

But the shock came when the door leading to their room bore the figures 13.

'Darling,' said the young bride, 'we can't possibly spend our honeymoon in room thirteen.' She was horrified.

So her husband arranged that they should have another room, and they were shown to number fifty-eight. Would that do?

It certainly would, they exclaimed happily.

They had a wonderful honeymoon, and later returned home. Then it suddenly dawned on them. Room fifty-eight (five plus eight is thirteen).

'Well, I never,' they laughed.

Have I said enough to arouse your interest? I hope so. I am sure you will never regret it, if you make numerology a sincere study. It won't be long before you are able to say like I did, 'You look like a three.'

I have often told people the number of the house they live in, the number of children in their family, the number of this and the number of that. And I am always right. As I said in a past chapter, think of a number between one and two hundred, and I will give you the number you thought of!

Numbers. Numbers. They are intriguing, full of meaning and fascination. Each number tells its own story, and when you know that story off by heart, you can look at a person and the secrets are laid bare, as it were. Study hard; it is going to help you a lot.

26
Prelude To Mind-Reading— Astrology

Do the stars play an important part in our lives? Is it possible to foretell events by studying the position of the stars and discovering their occult influence on human affairs? Can we judge the character of a person by knowing what stars he was born under?

Of course we can. Astrology is one of the most ancient beliefs; it prevailed from earliest times among the Chaldeans, Egyptians, Etruscans, Hindus and Chinese, and it had a powerful influence in the Europe of the Middle Ages.

In the Middle Ages astrology was brought to Europe by the Arabs and by the fifteenth century the ministers of the cult had become so powerful that no court was complete without its astrologer, and no monarch would dare to feast, fast, or fight unless assured that 'the stars were propitious'.

The first attempt to study the stars and to interpret their behaviour were made by the Babylonians. It was at one time believed in by men of such intelligence as **Tacitus** and **Johann Kepler**. There were few great families but what had an astrologer attached to them to read the horoscopes of any new member of the house.

Who was **Tacitus**? He was a Roman historian whose great

power lay in his insight into character (and this insight is what you want).

And **Johann Kepler**? Well, he was an astronomer. He lived in a **camera obscura** tent photographing the heavens. He studied 'the motions of the star' Mars, with calculations repeated seventy times. He discovered the planetary laws of the Universe, which are known as Kepler's Laws.

The stars were said by the old astrologers to have almost omnipotent influence on the lives and destinies of man.

According to astrology, those leading stars which are above the horizon at a person's birth influence his life and fortune; when those stars are in the ascendant, he is strong, healthy, and lucky; but when they are in the descendant, below the horizon, his stars do not shine on him; he is in the shade and subject to ill-fortune.

I want to arouse your interest in the stars and then we can see how we can apply it to mind-reading.

In judicial astrology the whole heaven is divided into twelve portions by means of great circles crossing the north and south points of the horizon, through which the heavenly bodies pass every twenty-four hours. Each of these divisions is called a **house**. These twelve **houses** each have their special functions. (1) **the house of life**; (2) **fortune and riches**; (3) **brethren**; (4) **parents and relatives**; (5) **children**; (6) **health**; (7) **marriage**; (8) **death**; (9) **religion**; (10) **dignities**; (11) **friends**; (12) **enemies**.

There is very much more to it than that, but I give you this insight because very few people realize anything at all about the stars, and how they can help in your life, and help you to read minds. I am telling you about them, because here is another vital clue to a person's character if you become proficient and understand it thoroughly.

The late Nell St John Montague was speaking on the telephone to a friend of mine. She had never met him, and knew nothing about him except that he was an author. After the conversation had been going some little while she suddenly said, 'Ah well, of course. You're a Virgo.'

This came as a bombshell, and my friend couldn't make out how on earth she knew, for she was right.

You can tell a person's star even by how they talk if you have made a keen study of the subject.

When you have the real knowledge of astrology, you can recognize dominant characteristics. You know that, born under a certain star, that person is predisposed to certain actions. You know their health tendencies and personality traits; know where and when they should invest; plan their present and future moves. Just as the moon influences the tides, so do the stars influence human beings. You can tell a person whom they should mix with, or marry, for lasting happiness.

You study a person's face; head, forehead, eyes, nose, and mouth; and from that you know plenty about them. You come, through a study of numerology, to know what number they are; and each number has its own story to tell. You now know a good bit more about them. Then astrology steps in, and you are able to say (or think) 'you are a Virgo'. You know all about Virgo characteristics, desires, behaviour, and with the help of what you've learnt from physiognomy and numerology, you have the whole perfect picture. You can 'sum up' the kind of thoughts that run through a head like this. The battle's half won.

Let's take a Sagittarius subject. You know they have a secretive nature; they rarely if ever share their troubles or triumphs with others. They might go much further if they did, but in a way it may rank as shyness. They are not the type to 'blow their own trumpet', which is almost a necessity in the rat-race of today.

You know that at times they have quite extraordinary mental energy. They are clever with money and have insight into financial matters. You know they are very courageous and brave in facing danger.

In summing them up, you know they are very house-proud, and like everything very tidy and beautiful. You know that the Sagittarius subject suffers from **astraphobia** – fear of thunderstorms. They do not like explosions or violence in any form.

You know that they suffer from rheumatism and that they are the nervous type. They get 'stage fright' if they have to meet a famous personality of stage or screen, or any celebrity, for that matter.

You know they need as much fruit as possible in their diet, and should practise breathing exercises. You know that their metal is Tin, their stone the Topaz, lucky number 3, and lucky day Thursday.

So what? Well, you have a lot there to work on. You memorize the meaning of each star, so that you can at once recognize these things in the appropriate subject. If a discussion is under way regarding some adventure that promises danger, you know that a Sagittarius subject will hold thoughts of courage and daring. They would dare anything, and the thought would be an adventurous one. You do see what I'm driving at, don't you?

You may be hard to convince, but do you realize that now, in the middle of the twentieth century, more people are reading their horoscopes than ever before?

Do people born the same time, the same day, the same year, lead similar lives? If so, let me tell you that in a national newspaper on October 24th, 1956, the story was told of two Yorkshiremen, Mr John Dill and Mr Horace Twivey, who were both born in Sheffield about 9 a.m. on October 19th, 1891.

They both followed the occupation of rent collector, Mr Dill with Adwick U.D. Council, and Mr Twivey with Don-caster Corporation. On reaching the age of sixty-five, each now being chief rent collector, they retired, and then discovered each other's existence and the close similarity of their lives.

I don't do anything important until the trend of the stars is right for me. I would not dream of doing anything vital when the moon is full.

It works out so well for me, that I keep a special diary for recording the trends of the stars, so that I can see instantly what dates to follow and which to avoid, when it comes to something very important.

If I entertain friends, I first consider the sign under which they were born, to see that there is no chance of conflict. I choose the day when everything promises to be particularly rosy.

You probably couldn't care less what I do, but people have a way of putting their hand on my shoulder with the exclamation, 'Koran, why are you always so lucky?'

It is interesting to study the stars in regard to famous people, and you can see how true they work out. Brigitte Bardot the famous film star was born under the sign of Libra, namely, between September 24th and October 23rd. This sign depicts that you will be attractive, with a craving for everything that is lovely in life, and a dislike for the sordid. Those born under Capricorn are ambitious, rising to their top form late in life. And they remain very youthful. The astrologers who formulated it could never have known that Dr Konrad Adenauer, born January 5th, 1876, would still be alive in 1964, or another Capricornian, Dr Albert Schweitzer, born January 14th, 1875.

Two more Capricornians, Gladstone, died at eighty-eight, and Lloyd George at eighty-two. They both lived long and active lives. Cary Grant, the film star, older than Dr Ramsey, the Archbishop of Canterbury, also remains very youthful physically and in looks. So you may remember, Capricornians live long, and remain youthful.

The people of Scorpio are concerned with power, not so much for their own sakes as for the good of the people. It so happens that under this sign come Montgomery, Nehru, de Gaulle, and born a few days after them, with Scorpio in the ascendant, under the planet Mars, we have Sir Winston Churchill. Power, then, for the subjects of Scorpio.

Are you impressed? It's wonderful, really, isn't it?

Kruschev, born under the sign of Aries (March 21st to April 20th). What of it? 'They carry out their undertakings with confidence and dash. The movements are quick and impulsive, the whole personality is intensely alive.' Isn't that a true picture? Mr Harold Wilson is very fond of going to an uninhabited island and makes a point of being utterly alone. He was born under the sign of Pisces, **my sign** (February 19th to March 20th), and like Harold Wilson, I do not like crowds; I enjoy being alone at times, and it is necessary for my work. Many people born under this sign shrink from society.

There are many people who run their lives by the stars, but you never hear about them. They don't go around telling everybody.

Catherine Boyle, the well-known television actress is a favourite with viewers. It is said that no doubt 'Katie' will have consulted her stars before she gets to her job, for she is a staunch believer in astrology and its influence on her life, and has long been a student of the stars.

She says, 'From the time I first learned about astrology from a pamphlet smuggled into school by a friend – and found myself to be born under Gemini, the sign of dual personality, mercurial temperament, and an adaptable, constantly curious mind – I have believed absolutely in its influence on our lives. For years now I have studied astrology carefully in relation to all I do. I look upon it as something in which there is a strong element of truth, remembering that it is an old and respectable belief.'

The Countess of Dartmouth (former Viscountess Lewisham) is a member of the Westminster Council, and she also believes in the stars.

'I often look up our horoscopes,' she says, 'before beginning the day. I am Virgo; my husband is Taurus. Experts say this is the ideal combination.'

One of Britain's finest sopranos is Lucille Graham. She was the first girl to sing on commercial television in this country, and she believes in astrology.

Lucille was cast to sing and play the part of the famous prima donna Adelina Patti when the B.B.C. televised Madame Patti's life story.

'You can get guidance from the stars that is helpful,' she says, 'but you are not compelled to follow it. The stars impel, but do not compel.'

She believes they are a means of discovering the purposes of life.

Then there is Jerry Desmonde, born under the sign of Cancer (the Crab). Jerry has made fame on television and films. He believes that everything in his life is predestined. Of that he is absolutely convinced.

It is linked, he believes, with astrology. He thinks our lives are largely written in advance, and some people are able to get inside information through the stars.

'My introduction to astrology came at one of the toughest times of my career,' he says. 'It was after the death of Sid Field, with whom I had been playing. A bitter shock to show business and to me personally. It left me out of a job, with no prospects.

'At a friend's suggestion I had my horoscope cast and an outline drawn up of the tendencies I could expect in the next three years.

'There wasn't one good patch in the astrologer's forecast, and this turned out to be entirely correct. Among the innumerable trends set out was the likelihood of my going to hospital. This was confirmed by an operation some time later for a stomach ulcer.

'Fortunately the stars have been much better placed for me lately. After a three years' prediction coming absolutely right, I need no other proof of the stars being heavily involved in my personal destiny.'

Now, have I convinced you that there is something in it?

And that astrology is not a subject for ridicule, but to be taken seriously. I hope you will go ahead and include this in your programme, because it will help you so much to know people; know them better than they know themselves. And you must be in the know, if you are going to read minds with any speed of accuracy.

How many people plot their days and their lives by the stars? We do not know, but we do see people getting well ahead, and others lagging hopelessly behind. It was Shakespeare who said, 'The fault, dear Brutus, is not in our stars, but in ourselves that we are underlings.'

Remember I said I always wear a solid gold ring, embossed with the signs of the Zodiac, in blue enamel. I am never without it.

Extract from **Fate** magazine:

'Certainly AL KORAN believes. He is the World's Greatest Mind-reader. He says:

"Much can be learned from the study of horoscopes. In my opinion one's life and destiny are strongly influenced by the Zodiacal signs under which one is born. I spend many hours delineating, as it is termed, horoscopes for my friends and acquaintances.

To watch the pattern of life unfold as one locates the houses and signs and positions of the planets in the horoscope wheel brings home the extent of the star's influence on our everyday lives. If you want success, believe in the wisdom of the stars." '

27
I Call It PURE PSYCHOLOGY

In addressing my audience from the stage, in answer to their puzzled expressions, I always say that what I have done is **pure psychology**. Anyone who has ever seen my performance has heard me say this.

Psychology is the study of human behaviour; from it you know why a person does a certain thing; acts in a certain way, or says what he does.

Here are a few extracts which emphasize this.

At the bottom of a long Press notice in the **Evening Express**, it says:

'**Koran, who bases his mind-reading on psychology, has amazed thousands of people by his act – The Power of Thought.**

And from the **Stage**:

'**How much is mind-reading and how much just magic doesn't seem to matter.**'

And again from the **Liverpool Echo**:

'**Koran, the man who created a sensation on television a short time ago, has an intriguing act to offer on his first appearance in Liverpool. He claims to perform, partly by psychology and partly by what he calls direct mind control.**'

The **Manchester Evening News** talk of my remarkable **mind-reading feats**, and the **Manchester Guardian**:

'**Al Koran defends his title as the world's fastest Mind-Reader.** . . . Modestly attributing his turn of speed to a dose of psychology or a pinch of auto-suggestion. . . .'

Psychology. Auto-suggestion. Direct Mind Control. I am not going to tell you how I do it, but I can give you some ideas how it may be done if you try it yourself. Take the performance I give where I use five envelopes; many viewers have seen it on television, as well as on stage.

In one envelope there is a £5 note. If any of the four volunteers from the audience select the envelope with the note in it, it is theirs.

They choose. Envelopes number 3, 1, 5, 4 have been handed out and I am left with number 2.

Maybe I give a quick 'once over' to the four contestants (I'm not saying), but I ask a man if he would like to change his envelope with mine (he looks like a **Leo** subject). That means he is a man who **can't make up his mind; indecisive attitude to life. It is hard, if not impossible, for such a man to be positive in matters that mean quick thinking. And he's got to think quick** (I know he can't do it). I repeat, 'Anybody like to change their minds?' then addressing him in particular, 'Would **you**?'

Of course he wouldn't.

I notice that the man with number 3 envelope in his hand looks like a **Libra. Enjoys a risk now and again, but never very successful,** so he won't chance it. He clings tight to the envelope he has in his hand.

I'm sure number 1 is a **Scorpio. Overdeveloped sense of his own importance. Thinks he knows best,** so sticks to it.

Nobody wants to change their envelopes for mine. Right. I open it. There you are – the £5 note! I had 'summed them up' by their faces, their hands, their carriage, and I knew this is what would happen. I haven't studied the stars or character from faces, for nothing!

Now, I don't say this is the way I do it, though it would probably appear so to you. But a knowledge of physiognomy and astrology gives you something definite to work on, and that is what I am trying to impress upon you. It's pure psychology; a knowledge of how certain people are likely to behave. Mind-reading plus deduction.

I say to the Press in the Bulletin, September 19th, 1957:

'People, it seems, have a mass mind and presented with, say, a choice of five numbered envelopes, the average person will normally pick one placed in a certain position. So, without looking, I can tell which one they've taken.'

Easy, when you know how, isn't it?

From the Scottish Daily Mail:

'A television favourite, Koran, billed as "the world's fastest mind-reader", gave an uncanny performance.

Drawing out four from the audience, he asked them to describe their dream car, then opened an envelope, held in full view throughout, and the description of the car was written inside.'

No, I won't tell you how I do it. This is not a book on how I work magic, but how to bring magic out of your own mind.

I have found that when I ask a person on the stage to name a number between one and a hundred, an individual, in a moment of mental panic, will give only one of five numbers – repetition numbers, I call them, impressed on the mind over the years. The five numbers differ with the person. Pure psychology.

Another extract, this time from the Halifax Daily Courier and Guardian, September 6th, 1957:

'. . . Hardly before the preliminary conversational canters were finished, he handed me a piece of paper, asked me to write down the date of my birth and then, without a by-your-leave, tore it up and let the pieces flutter to the floor. Over cups of tea he talked about fast driving at night (his favourite pastime) and then, without any encouraging clucks from this canny spectator, and within the space of thirty seconds, he told me the date of my birth.

"How?" I queried. He dismissed the idea of mind-reading with: "A combination of suggestion and psychology, the moment of truth which is there on most occasions between two people."

Through childhood, schooldays, and adolescence he constantly reminded himself and others that his psychic hunches were not merely parlour tricks but powers to be treated with the highest respect.'

I use people and categorize them into five groups. On the two fringes are the mentally deranged and the geniuses. In the middle, in non-technical terms, the slow, medium, and quick-witted.

As a person approaches I deftly place him into one of these three groups, ask him to think of a number, and human beings, ever-changing creatures of habit, the man invariably thinks of one of three numbers, the three numbers different in each group. It is at that moment that I use suggestion, psychology, the moment of truth, and a slice of my own subconscious.

A woman writes her child's name and locks it in a box. 'Take this dictionary,' I said to someone. 'Go outside the room and look up a word.' Did I tell him the right one? I did. Three times and no stooges. I ask people in the audience to pick a word from the dictionary, and then I tell them what it is. I am right every time. But I'm not telling you how I do it.

What we see with the eyes is no more real than the story of Santa Claus or the Stork. I want to tell you, though you must already know it, that it is not the eye that sees. When we dream we see without eyes and hear without ears and not only see and hear, but we see and hear things and come in contact with people and places which are not there!

The eyes are only instruments. What we actually see with is our other self; our **double**. That is the self which knows and feels and sees.

285

To get a better grasp at what I am driving at, let me remind you that it has often been said that a man feels his amputated leg as though it were still there. It is the invisible psychic leg which he feels **and which is real to him**.

We can all **see without eyes**. Perhaps you did not know this. When I was a little boy, my Aunt lost her engagement ring. She was in a terrible state over it, until I said I **saw** it in the bottom drawer in her bedroom chest. And there it was. I was always **seeing** things, in this way.

And the day is not far distant when we shall be able to **see** with our fingers. There are hundreds of people even now (the late Edgar Wallace was said to be one of them) who can pick up a letter and **see** its contents by touch before they have opened it. They will know if the letter contains good news or bad and from what part of the world it comes. One's fingers are going to be trained to **see** by feeling. Soon we may all be **seeing without eyes** as the psychometrist does when he or she handles a glove, a string of beads, or any other article, in order to **see** what has happened in your past and what is going to happen in your future.

This is nothing new. Many great personalities have trained themselves to get marvellous results in this way.

It is easy to cultivate this **seeing without eyes**. Try it. If you want to wake two hours earlier in the morning, then tell yourself when you go to bed that you want to wake up at, say, five o'clock. And you will! On the very stroke. You are able to **see** the time without your eyes open and know when to get up if you want to. It is all very simple. All you have to do is remember that it is a matter of **belief** and making up your mind.

Dr Gilbert Scott once made a very clever experiment. At four o'clock one morning he asked a nurse who was with him to close her eyes and in her imagination to go to a certain railway station and tell him the time by the clock on the platform.

'Four twenty-one,' she said. She had her eyes firmly shut.

'No,' he answered her. 'You're wrong. It's not four twenty-one, it's half-past four.'

But he took her watch to the station and on comparison discovered that it was nine minutes fast. How did she know the time. Even if human beings can transmit thought, a clock cannot.

Perhaps the answer lies in what I have written – she was **seeing without eyes.**

Oriental scientists say that we can **see without eyes.** They have actually proved that a person can close their eyes or wear a tight blindfold, and actually thread a needle of cotton. It takes a lot of believing, but it has happened more than once.

In the same way a book held before closed eyes has been read. The subject is first hypnotized, but we are reminded that there is such a thing as **self-hypnosis.** In this somnambulistic state you can perform anything, like the girl who read an open book (while her eyes were blindfold) placed a little distance away from her. When a man stood in front of the book to block her view, she was unable to read. When he told her to 'read over his shoulder', she did so perfectly. No limits are set as to what marvels you can perform in this state, even under self-hypnosis. You can perform magic.

An old Buddhist monk made an astonishing discovery. It was that we can **see with our cheeks.** Qualified scientists took the matter up and actually proved this to be true. Children were trained to read and thread needles completely blindfold, and blind people did the same thing. 'Vision' was received through the skin of the cheek. It has been proved that the cheek has optical nerves.

And it was discovered that if meditation was practised prior to this magic, it came easier and quicker, and in some cases the blind would spend many weeks in training, meditating and developing a keen concentration. Like this, the skin of their cheeks became more sensitive and in time they were **seeing without eyes** and in colour, they could distinguish the colour of a lady's dress, and holding the needle close to the cheek, a blindfold subject could see to thread it. A woman whose face was covered with cream and powder could not do this, as the cheek must be naturally clean. Remember I said it was a Buddhist monk who discovered this, and the Buddhists are all for meditation. You can meditate on this marvel in the quiet of your own little room.

Work regularly and persistently with this idea of eyeless vision, with a consistent energy and determination that nothing can daunt, and you can take it from me that if you have true faith in your ability to succeed, you most surely will, easily and quickly. Meditation in all acts of magic is the thing. Practise and keep on practising. Welcome the idea, not as ridiculous, but as a glorious possibility, then soon 'what eyes have not seen (your eyes) shall be established unto you'.

Another Press report of mine says:

'Al deals with all types of people in his act. "I divide them into three main classes. There are the 10 per cent 'dead mugs', the 80 per cent ordinary people, and the 10 per cent clever boys who know it all.

And who do you think falls the hardest? The clever boys. They are so certain they'll see through it, they don't see it coming." '

I repeat, it's pure psychology.

You have read this book; you may think it all too impossible; too much of a fight.

Let me remind you that the greatest battle ever fought was won by a Galilean carpenter.

Go Forward, with a splendid heart.

Other recommended books...

HOW TO DEVELOP A SUPER POWER MEMORY

Harry Lorayne. However poor you may *think* your memory is now, the author believes that you have a memory *10 to 20 times more powerful than you realize!* He maintains that your memory is working at a tiny fraction of its true power today—because *you simply don't know the right way to feed it facts!* Because you don't know the right way to take names and faces and anything else you want to remember—*and burn them into your memory so vividly that you can never forget them!* The most practical, lucid and effective memory-training book ever published.

HOW TO READ A PERSON LIKE A BOOK

THE ART OF NON-VERBAL COMMUNICATION

Nierenberg & Calero. *Illustrated.* Gestures—postures—facial expressions—body movements are *body language*. Here's how to read body language to keep a controlling hand in arguments and negotiations; decide when the other person is lying; interpret gestures of friendliness or flirtation; detect boredom; understand gestures that have double meanings. This non-verbal communication enables you to discover *what's behind a person's words!* The authors held hundreds of seminars and have recorded 2,500 negotiating situations.

IN SEARCH OF THE HEALING ENERGY

Mary Coddington. *Your* illnesses could be cured by acupuncture, homoeopathy, Reichian therapeutics, and other therapies described here—all employing healing energy emanating from one's own body! This force penetrates everything. Hahnemann termed it *the vital force,* Reich, *orgone energy.* These rays prove that the human body is as much energy (waves) as it is mass (solid particles). Now discover what this power can do for *you!* *Amazing contents include:* How acupuncture cures by balancing the body's *ch'i* energy; Homoeopathic drugs stimulate self-cure; Did Wilhelm Reich find the secret of creation?

INSTANT MIND POWER

PROGRAMME YOUR MIND FOR SUCCESS!

Harry Lorayne. This is not a book in the normal sense of the word. It comprises a series of over 2,300 simple interlocking exercises in which *you,* the reader, actively participate by providing written answers to key questions. Gradually, as the power of your mind builds and expands like a giant dynamo gaining momentum, you can build a will of iron; make people do what you want; make bad habits break themselves; make one hour do the work of two; create winning ideas; flash-learn anything; develop steel-shutter concentration; develop "X-ray" powers of observation.

CENTERING

THE POWER OF MEDITATION

S. G. Laurie & M. J. Tucker. Unique system of integrating the whole personality, using meditation techniques for reducing stress, extending awareness, increasing learning power and understanding, discovering your latent psychic abilities. The 'failures' you are currently experiencing are the results of faulty imaginings in your past. You have programmed yourself—unconsciously—for these situations. This book shows how to change them by becoming a psychically 'centered' individual—healthy, happy, financially secure. *Includes:* Brain waves and meditation; Breath control and posture in meditation; Finding your true self; Retraining the subconscious; Healing energy; Personal moral codes; Working with dreams.

PENDULUM POWER

YOUR ENTRANCE INTO THE WORLD OF INTUITIVE AWARENESS

G. Nielsen & J. Polansky. How to make a pendulum and practise mysterious radiesthesia! Choose a career, find romance, pin-point physical and mental illness, enhance *all* aspects of living—with pendulum power! Here is a practical overview for beginners in this master science in which Higher Intelligence communicates through the nervous system, using a pendulum to amplify the signal—a new way of using the mind. *Contents include:* Why the pendulum works; True stories of pendulum power; The pendulum, your work and your career; The pendulum and dynamic self-healing; The pendulum and meditation.

PSI-KINETIC POWER:

MAGIC ROAD TO RICHES

Sandra McNeil, the 'people's psychic', here reveals how to create a life of abundant wealth, perfect health, true love and unbounded happiness with Psi-Kinetic Power—the energy of the psychic mind in motion! 'You possess a power so great', says Sandra McNeil, 'that it is like having your own invisible servant . . . to work for you . . . grant your every wish'. *Galvanizing contents include:* Your thoughts are electrical power lines; Your Magic Pulsator; Magic Pulsator exercise to change your physical appearance; How to design your P-K Money Kite; How to create your own magical Bubble of Protection.

PYRAMID POWER

SECRET ENERGY OF THE ANCIENTS REVEALED

M. Toth & G. Nielsen. The most up-to-date source material available on pyramidology! Gives detailed instructions for 3 methods of pyramid construction. Pyramids—even cardboard ones—generate physical and spiritual energy, preserve foodstuffs, sharpen razor blades, stimulate psychic power! Also reveals the results of some fascinating experiments and suggests a number of simple experiments for the reader—which scientists have performed in their laboratories.